# Archdeacon Grantly Walks Again

*Trollope's Clergy Then and Now*

— MICHAEL HIGGINS —

Sacristy
Press

**Sacristy Press**
PO Box 612, Durham, DH1 9HT

www.sacristy.co.uk

First published in 2024 by Sacristy Press, Durham

Sacristy Limited, registered in England
& Wales, number 7565667

**British Library Cataloguing-in-Publication Data**
A catalogue record for the book is
available from the British Library

ISBN 978-1-78959-331-0

# Contents

# Foreword

An affection for the novels of Anthony Trollope as well as the Church of England inspires this delightful collection of portraits of fictional (but believable) clergy. Michael Higgins shows an intimate familiarity with the wide range of Trollope's clerical creations. He also illustrates how they have their equivalents in the contemporary Church of England in his own clerical sketches. It is a fascinating conceit, and perhaps that word is apposite in its other meaning too, since there are some very conceited men among those depicted here.

Although many of Trollope's clergy are flawed and a few deeply unpleasant, he makes them more believable by giving most of them a few redeeming features. Archdeacon Grantly has a softer heart than outward appearances suggest, and he is capable of changing his mind, despite seeming initially so obdurate. Even Obadiah Slope, the unctuous bishop's chaplain, is given a slight benefit of the doubt by Trollope who comments that "when promoting his own interests he did promote the religion in which he believed". The contemporary equivalent of Mr Slope, Adrian Booth, is one of the least fully drawn characters in the Higgins collection of clergy, but like Slope we do not see him in maturity but only in his early years. After Slope leaves Barchester, we are told that he marries, and Trollope allows us to hope that he will learn from his fall from grace, perhaps through the blessing of a good wife. One hopes Adrian has married well too. Wisely, we are left to speculate.

Trollope is skilful enough to make his "good" characters interesting. Septimus Harding is perhaps the most lovable clergyman in the whole of English literature, but there is nothing whatever dull about him. His whimsical humour reveals his perception. David Ward, the modern reflection of the warden of Hiram's Hospital, has a more demanding pastoral job but loves and is loved in his parish, exemplifying what many English people still want in their vicar. Francis Arabin, another of Trollope's "good" clergy, is a reserved character and thus not easy to lift from the page. It is the interweaving of his life with others in Barchester which gives him a growing humanity, one well reflected in the academic-turned-parish-priest Matthew Gibbs, his modern reflection here.

What adds to the appeal of this volume is that the contemporary clergy depicted are not slavish adaptations of Trollope's creations. They inhabit different worlds, come from different backgrounds, and face issues (e.g. Robert Bolter's brush with safeguarding) which would perplex even the most reform-minded nineteenth-century churchman. As with most of Trollope's clergy, Michael Higgins presents us with clergy in their prime rather than at the beginning of their ministry. They are almost all university-educated and trained for ordination in residential theological colleges rather than on one of the many non-residential courses. London Clubs have a profile which belongs more to the twentieth rather than the twenty-first century, for the Church of England is now changing again. Whether the Church of England herself will continue to be quite so lovable in the coming century is a question, perhaps unintended, which the author provoked me to ponder. This book is an elegy to faithful, if flawed, clergy of every generation. As the author observes, human nature does not change, and both a novelist and an observant clerical writer unite here in recognizing that reality.

**The Rt Revd Graham James**

# Preface

Anthony Trollope knew only too well the difficulty of exploring in words the heights and depths of human personality. Introducing a complicated figure in a chapter of his best-known novel *Barchester Towers,* he writes: "How often does the novelist feel . . . that he has conceived within his mind and accurately depicted on the tablet of his brain the full character and personage of a man . . . till at the end of a dozen pages the man described has no more resemblance to the man conceived than the signboard at the corner of the street has to the Duke of Cambridge?" Yet it is precisely because of his awareness of this difficulty that Trollope is the writer known above all else for his brilliance in creating characters that walk off the page. To him they were living flesh and blood. He tells us what delight he had in writing *Barchester Towers*: "The Bishop and Mrs Proudie were very real to me, as were the troubles of the Archdeacon and the loves of Mr. Slope."

Trollope's exploration of human nature includes a whole galaxy of characters from doctors to dukes, but his most perceptive writing majored on the clergy of the Church of England in all their great variety. He wrote 47 novels in which 53 different clergy appeared, and never tired of showing that, while clergy are sometimes thought to be holy people, the highs and lows of the human condition are as much at work in them as in other people. These pages visit 12 of Trollope's clergy creations, where snobbery, jealousy, ambition and devotion to filthy lucre sit alongside love, kindness and generosity in similar proportions as in the rest of the human race.

Trollope's priests served in a Church of England very different from our own day. Congregations were far larger, while the Church played a central part in national life. Bishops were powerful figures in Parliament, while the parish clergy played a central role in local affairs and were often magistrates. The Church was a wealthy institution, with the majority of clergy Oxbridge educated and from upper middle-class stock, comfortable in the higher echelons of society.

Yet despite altered circumstances human nature never changes. To illustrate this simple fact vividly, alongside each of Trollope's characters sketches of contemporary clergy have been added. The Trollopian priests and these modern clergy who sit alongside them share two simple facts. First, both are utterly fictitious: there was no Archdeacon Grantly and there is no Archdeacon Roberts. However, the contemporary creations, while being fictitious, are hopefully authentic, the result of a lifetime of working with and observing clergy at all levels. Second, both groups feature only male priests; sadly, women priests were unknown in Trollope's day.

This small volume has been fun to produce, and it is hoped Trollope fans will have fun reading it. Others may be introduced to the great Anthony for the first time while church folk might learn a little more about their clergy.

# Acknowledgements

Like many books published recently, this small offering was written to while away the time during the Great Covid Lockdown of 2020/1. It was fun to produce, and I hope will be fun to read. I owe more than I can express to the support and encouragement of my wife Margaret during those months I was locked away at the computer, and to our lawyer daughter Gabrielle for her expert help with proof reading.

My friend Canon Stuart Nairn, former Vicar of Castle Acre in Norfolk, read an early draft. He is expert in spotting typographical errors, and his many corrections were much appreciated.

The Venerable Christopher Skilton, former Archdeacon of Croydon, carefully read the text and made helpful comments. He is a priest of great experience and a keen Trollope reader, and he offered valuable suggestions on both the Trollopian and contemporary character sketches.

I am particularly grateful to the Right Reverend Graham James, former Bishop of Norwich, for writing a Foreword. I deeply appreciate his kind words.

I have also been well supported by the staff of the Sacristy Press as the manuscript was being prepared for publication, and in particular by the encouragement given me by Dr Natalie Watson, Publishing Director at Sacristy Press.

**Michael Higgins**
*1 August 2023*

## The Trollope biographies are taken from

*Barchester Towers*

*The Warden*

*Last Chronicle of Barset*

*The Vicar of Bullhampton*

*Miss Mackenzie*

*Is he Popenjoy?*

*Framley Parsonage*

*Trollope: Autobiography*

# The Pauper

## The Reverend Josiah Crawley

Clergy are no different from the rest of the human race; the way we cope with trials and tribulations reveals our true character. Josiah Crawley faced disappointment in life, coping with extreme poverty and facing a criminal charge of stealing a cheque—all at the same time. What manner of man he was is revealed by the way he dealt with these matters.

We first meet Crawley at the start of his clerical career as vicar of a parish in Cornwall. A close friend from his Oxford days, Francis Arabin, is also a priest and now an academic and Fellow of an Oxford College. Arabin was wrestling with the temptation to become a Roman Catholic and travels down to Cornwall to face his problems by the peace of the Cornish coast. There he meets up again with Crawley who gives him helpful counsel and advice which results in him remaining in the Church of England. Throughout his life, Arabin remained conscious of the great debt of gratitude he owed his old friend for his wisdom at this time.

As the years move on, the direction of travel of the two men is very different. Arabin becomes a dignitary of the Church and Dean of Barchester, while Crawley continues toiling away in remote Cornwall, a move to another parish long overdue. Happily, the dean has the power of appointment to a parish near Barchester, and his old friend moves from Cornwall to become Perpetual Curate of Hogglestock—in effect the vicar but of a poorly endowed parish. Now later in life, Crawley is filled with disappointment. It was hard to bear that Arabin is now a senior priest living in a comfortable deanery in the Cathedral Close, while he only has his poor parish with a tumble-down vicarage and that only through his grand friend's kindness. Crawley feels he has failed in life, his frustration made worse by the fact that poverty and the need to support a wife and family make him dependent on gifts of money from Arabin.

He reacts not with gratitude but by constantly comparing his academic ability to that of his friend. He received a First Class degree at Oxford, while Arabin had to be content with a Second. He knows Hebrew; Arabin knows no Hebrew. He delights in taking down a peg those above him, who have been more successful in life than he has. When a titled neighbour, Lady Lufton, wants her own vicar ticking off for spending time in the hunting field—in those days viewed as a grave failing in a priest—she chooses Crawley to do the job. It is a task he greatly enjoys and rushes over to his prosperous victim's house without losing any time. Similarly, when the bishop writes telling him to stand down from taking services in his church because of the criminal charge hanging over him, he much enjoys sending a brilliant and closely argued response, showing clearly and correctly that the bishop is exceeding his powers. Unhappy with this response, the bishop summons him to the palace. Crawley looks forward to "crushing" the bishop in person, and when he succeeds in doing exactly this, he smiles at the bishop's discomfort, the smile of a clever but disappointed man working off his disappointment.

This combination of career failure and coping with poverty in a poorly paid parish eats into his soul. The result is a constant need to remind others of what he sees as his inherent superiority, accompanied by a constant desire to assert himself. He is occasionally forced to accept money from Arabin but turns away all other offers of help with pride. How dare his neighbour Lord Lufton come to him "with his paltry money in his hand", while other offers get the same treatment. He views poverty as a disgrace and begging a crime. When his wife gets gifts of fruit and produce from neighbours, their arrival is shrouded in secrecy, lest Crawley should send them away. Poverty leads him to assume constant humility in the presence of those better placed than he; he wears his rusty old cloak with ostentatious bitterness. But it is all false humility, masking crushing pride. He knows poverty cannot take away his social standing both as a Church of England priest and as a gentleman and therefore never fails to remind others of these things by his bearing and conduct. No opportunity of standing on his dignity and status is allowed to pass; we find him reminding a visitor he is sorry he cannot provide him with a better horse or that he is unable to provide the hospitality he would like to dispense. Even when summoned to court to face the theft allegation, he draws attention to himself by demanding to be taken there by official carriage, refuses to sit in court, insists on standing throughout and objects to engaging a lawyer. It is not a pretty picture.

Although his mind remains clear and agile, Crawley becomes an over-sensitive introspective priest, almost basking in grief. Wrestling with disappointment, poverty and the criminal charge make him deeply depressed and moody. He spends hours sitting over a dying fire in his vicarage, looking back on his life and on what the future holds. Deeply pessimistic, he says when first told of the theft accusation "I suppose by tonight I'll be in prison" and sees himself as a "hunted beast". He tells Henry Grantly a suitor for the hand of his daughter Grace, that his criminal actions mean he has forfeited all parental rights and so is unable as a father to give permission for the marriage. Much of his time is spent endlessly reflecting on how the cheque he is accused of stealing came into his possession in the first place, something of which he has no clear memory.

Crawley becomes strange, withdrawn and odd to such a degree that many of his friends and neighbours think he is mad. He has no close friends among his peers—a result of his poverty, his status as a potential criminal, and his character—but he does form deep friendships with a group of manual workers in the brickfields of his poor parish and regularly receives solace and comfort from them. There he is told he must have been "wool-gathering" when he took the cheque and that everything can be put down to his scholarly nature and being mesmerized by Greek, Latin and theology. Convinced this is the case, he concludes he has no option but to resign his parish—and this even before his court case has been heard. His private meditations lead him to decide he is no longer a fit person to hold office in the Church, despite the fact that a senior local priest, asked by the bishop to chair a commission looking into the whole matter, tells him his conclusion is premature, will result in his wife and family becoming destitute and that his proposed action results from sheer pride. Yet he persists, posting two resignation letters, one to the bishop and the other to friend Arabin, who appointed him.

Crawley wallows in his problems. He is a totally self-centred priest who never considers the effect of his behaviour on his long-suffering and devoted wife. Mrs Crawley has a great deal to bear, particularly after her husband tells her that for him there is only one way out of the situation. She starts to watch him carefully, fearing he might take his own life. Month after month she sits with him, comforts him and ekes out the housekeeping from their slender resources without a word of complaint. If a friend provides a carriage for her to return home, she alights a little way from their door, so as not to offend Josiah with an apparent display of opulence.

Through all his troubles, Crawley is deeply conscientious in his parish duties. He visits his flock regularly, teaches in the church school, takes time to prepare for worship and seems a model clergyman with a life undergirded by hours spent in private prayer and meditation. Yet all this devotion to duty and holiness appears hollow when set alongside his total inner dedication to himself and abiding concern about the image he cuts before others.

The cheque allegation comes to an end even before the matter comes up at the Assizes, where Crawley had been committed for trial. Again, Arabin is involved. One day he had put some bank notes in an envelope as a gift for Crawley who was going through a particularly hard time. Unknown to the generous dean, his wife Eleanor had slipped the cheque into the envelope as an additional gift for the poor man. If it had not been for the fact that, during the preliminary stages of the case before the magistrates, Arabin and his wife had both been away on the Continent, the case would never have got as far as it did.

Happily, Crawley's future changes dramatically. He gives his permission for the marriage of his daughter to Henry, the archdeacon's son, and the archdeacon marks the establishment of his innocence by presenting him to a prosperous plum parish in his gift. Yet even now his inner nature does not become any more attractive. Asked to choose as a gift new smart clerical clothing to match his new life, he chooses the most expensive while quickly relegating poverty to the past by becoming instantly at home as a guest in Archdeacon Grantley's comfortable rectory. The archdeacon demonstrates his mastery of the situation, marking Crawley's entry into his new life by presenting him with a book of sermons by his father, who had been a bishop. He tells him: "You and I are both gentlemen." The archdeacon judged well that this joint tribute to Crawley's scholarship and his love of status would tickle the vanity of this priest totally taken up with himself.

Bishops have always had to cope with mad, bad and sad priests. Crawley is never a bad man, although at times he may have been on the verge of madness. Yet he is most certainly a sad man and no great beacon of priestly virtue.

## The Reverend David Lloyd

David Lloyd has been vicar of a small town in Cheshire for the past five years. He is not well. He has lost all enthusiasm for his work, goes about his daily tasks as if in a dream and no longer enjoys life. He appears to be on the edge of depression. He has always been a deeply spiritual man, a biblical scholar, and a priest who spends much time in prayer and meditation. Yet Susan, his wife, now notices that while David is still faithful in his spiritual life, he spends long hours in his study, not praying or reading but moping and feeling sorry for himself.

Deep down David feels inadequate socially. His ultra-middle class parish is mainly commuting territory for Manchester and Liverpool. His people are mainly executives in city companies, lawyers, accountants, teachers, academics or some kind of professionals, living in comfortable housing and enjoying an affluent lifestyle. Whatever may go on underneath, the majority are confident and outgoing; social life in the area thrives, and there are always drinks or dinner parties going on somewhere. Many of the men are in the Round Table or the Rotary Club; the tennis and golf clubs both have waiting lists for membership and are mini-social centres themselves. The local schools are excellent, although many families send their children to fee-paying schools.

David feels like the proverbial fish out of water. Brought up in a poor Liverpool suburb, his father was a lorry driver and his mother a shop worker; he absorbed few social graces at home. A bright child from the local grammar school, he eventually won a place at Cambridge to study history but made few friends there. Spending most of his waking hours in the college library over the whole of his three university years, he managed totally to elude the middle-class brush and emerged from his student days with much the same kind of finesse as he had entered them. He recalls that on one of his rare appearances in the college bar before dinner in hall, a loud-mouthed Etonian had proclaimed to his fellow drinkers in a confident public voice: "Ho! Ho! Here's David come among us. He never went to school at all." He never entered that bar again. Later, he was accepted as a candidate for ordination and served a long curacy in a down-market parish in his native Liverpool before arriving in his Cheshire parish.

He has never been happy and the only folk with whom he really feels at ease are a few residents in a small area of council housing on the edge of the parish. He enjoys visiting here, because the people he meets are like those of his own early days in Liverpool—in fact many of them have been rehoused in the parish from that city. Here there are blunt, down-to-earth characters, kind, generous people who are above all unpretentious, the sort of folk to whom he warms. The fact is he feels ill at ease with the rest of his parishioners. David had been invited to a few dinner parties when he arrived, but invitations to these and other social events soon dried up—it was as if people realized he just didn't fit in. He has never been asked to join the Rotary Club. Church council meetings are a special agony, as most of the people round the table are more at ease and confident than the chairman; he often needs to pray for special strength before these occasions and has to steel himself to conduct the business of the evening. Daily life has become an agony, and Susan is aware of her husband withdrawing into his shell more and more as the months go past. Nor is life made any easier by constant financial worry and the threat that Susan might have to go out to work to make ends meet. Keeping up appearances in an affluent parish is difficult with a wife and three hungry young mouths to feed and clothe.

You might ask how this man has landed in such a parish. The answer is simple. The one friend he made at the church college where he had trained as a priest had understood his problems and befriended him. The two men have kept in touch, and James Elliot is now vicar of a large parish in Cheltenham; he has married a bishop's daughter, and his progress to a desirable parish in a desirable area has been rapid. By contrast, David had continued as a curate in Liverpool for five years, where his bishop appeared to take little interest in him. Despite several letters to the bishop asking for a move, no parish was ever suggested for him, and David was reluctant to take on another curacy. In desperation, he wrote to James in Cheltenham who immediately arranged through his father-in-law for David to be seen by the bishop of the next-door diocese to Liverpool, Chester. His interview there had been short and dramatic. The bishop had asked him a few cursory questions, noted he had a degree in history from Cambridge and that his own bishop had written well of him, and after 20 minutes David had emerged as vicar-designate of a smart Cheshire parish. It had not even been suggested he should view it before his appointment, while the churchwardens had simply been informed by the bishop of the name of their new vicar. It had not been an ideal process, and no thought was given to whether David and the parish were the right "mix". The bishop simply felt good at helping this stray curate find a niche, while it had been convenient for him to fill the parish with the least possible effort. At the same time, David was relieved to have found a move at last, and James basked in the sunshine of helping his friend.

In recent months, a far more serious cloud has descended on our already unhappy vicar. One of the more prosperous parishioners saw him in the church putting his arms around a crying choirboy to comfort him after he had been bawled at by an angry choirmaster for singing out of tune. Perhaps thinking this might be a key to getting what he thought of as "our unfortunate vicar" moved on elsewhere, this parishioner then wrote to the bishop suggesting David might have behaved improperly in embracing a choirboy in this way and asking whether there might be more behind the action. David was immediately interviewed by the diocesan safeguarding officer, with the unspoken suggestion his unfortunate behaviour might need to be investigated further. This development came as a massive shock, and David felt that everything was being blown up out of proportion. He had to wait two months to hear if the matter was to be taken further and whether he would need to be suspended from parish duties while this happened. He told Susan of this unfortunate state of affairs, and she too became desperately worried about their future.

Happily, things have now taken a massive turn for the better. The bishop has written to say the incident with the choirboy will not be taken further, but warning David to take much greater care in such matters. The bishop underlined in a formal letter that in an age where some priests have drawn the Church into ill repute, all priests need to be especially careful in their conduct, especially with children and young people. Even better, James—with whom David has kept in regular touch and who has been a tower of strength to him—has been to visit him in Cheshire. He now realizes this parish is not the right one for his friend and has registered David's deep unhappiness. Once again, James has consulted his bishop father-in-law who has promised in the near future to find a more appropriate appointment for David. Help seems to be on the horizon for this very troubled man.

# 2

# The Hen-Pecked Husband

## The Right Reverend Thomas Proudie, Bishop of Barchester

"The Bishop's Gambit" is the title of an episode in the BBC sitcom *Yes, Minister*. The prime minister is appointing a new bishop and asks if the candidate he is suggesting has had sufficient parish experience for the post. "Good heavens, no, Prime Minister", comes the response. "Clergymen who want to be bishops try to avoid pastoral work." However, the prime minister is assured the candidate has an "eminently suitable" wife – she is the daughter of the Earl of Chichester."

Thomas Proudie is an ambitious man; his pathway to the top has followed a similar strategy with effective results. He drew the income from a country parish but never went there, engaging a curate to do the work in his absence. Determined to wear the purple he knew that living in London was essential, where he was in daily touch with the "movers and shakers" of both political and ecclesiastical worlds. As secretary to various Church and government committees, his face became well known in metropolitan circles, and his skill in producing well-honed letters, papers and reports did not go unnoticed. Add a constant desire to please and be of service along with the fact that he and his wife were both distantly related to titled aristocratic families, and you have the perfect mix.

Yet this admirable pedigree on its own was not quite enough. To Dr Proudie's own ambition must be added that of his wife, a lady determined to preside over a bishop's palace and be covered with her husband's reflected glory. It was she who guided his steps on the upward path, made sure every advantage that came his way was exploited to the full and every friendship and contact called into maximum service. Some years later, following her early death, he reflected that his interests had always been her interests. Without her, he would never have been a bishop.

Now Dr Proudie is Bishop of Barchester, it might be thought the couple had achieved all they could have desired. Not so. Still ambitious, the new bishop hopes to move in time in an even higher sphere, perhaps in a bigger diocese or even to become an archbishop. With this in mind, he continues to keep up an expensive establishment in London along with a coach appropriate for his status, planning to be away from the diocese for many weeks during the London season. One incidental result of a continual drain on family financial resources is a loss of popularity with local tradesmen who missed his regular custom. Dr Proudie's predecessor never moved from the town.

The new bishop is a good-looking man; spruce and dapper, and very tidy . . . his features are well formed and he is proud of his fine mouth and chin. Although below middle height, he carries himself well, and if you met him, you would have liked what you saw, which would have pleased him, because his main aim in life is to please. For this reason, his religion is above all tolerant, an "all things to all men" type of faith; he bears with the idolatry of Rome . . . and is hand in glove with Presbyterian Synods. Above all Dr Proudie is concerned to cultivate dignity and gravitas. He is not a man to allow anything to be omitted that might be becoming to his new dignity. He understands well the value of forms, and that the due observance of rank cannot be maintained unless the trappings belonging to it are held in proper esteem. Here is a man who goes to great lengths to ensure he projects the right image. At every church service, the bishop, if present, pronounces the blessing at the end of worship. Dr Proudie, to ensure he makes the words as impressive as possible, practises them in his bedroom. We are not told if he does this in front of the mirror clad in full bishop's robes, but it is likely. Following his first visit to the bishop's palace, Dr Grantly the Archdeacon of Barchester, an expert in back-handed compliments, remarked that the new bishop seemed to have "moved among gentlemen", a deliciously accurate comment, indicating that his new bishop falls somewhat short of the real thing.

Trollope, in his verbal picture of the bishop, tells us it was no fault of his own if he had not a commanding eye, for he studies to assume it. The man is weak, indecisive and spineless, in small things and in large. When a controversial sermon preached in the cathedral by his chaplain stirred up the whole town, he and Mrs Proudie fled swiftly to London rather than face the fall-out, while on another occasion he avoided a difficult meeting with the archdeacon by making his chaplain answer the door and plead feigned illness.

Unfortunately for Thomas Proudie, two people in his household are bent on taking full advantage of their lord and master's feeble irresolute character. Both aspired to be Acting Bishop of Barchester. The first is his wife, the lady whose artful scheming placed him on his episcopal throne in the first place, and the second his resident chaplain, Obadiah Slope. A good deal of the bishop's time is spent first in agreeing with the proposal of one party, then changing his mind and agreeing with the other, constantly playing them off against each other while trying to decide which plan might serve him best. It must be an exhausting life, and no wonder that after some years of such wearing experience he tells his wife: "I wish I had never come to Barchester."

The bishop's inbuilt weakness of character has cost him dear in emotional strain, none more than in the perplexing saga of Josiah Crawley, a priest who has appeared before Barchester magistrates charged with stealing a cheque. Mr Crawley on one occasion told his wife that Dr Proudie was "led by the nose by his wife, weak as water, timid and vacillating". Mrs Proudie is aware of these views and is determined they should cost this priest dear. As soon as the unfortunate man is committed for trial at the coming Assizes, she urges the bishop to inhibit Mr Crawley from taking any further services in his church at Hogglestock, despite the fact he continually tells her he has no legal power to do so because the accused has not yet been proved guilty. The poor man painfully agonizes over the dilemma his wife has placed him in and finally decides, with much hand-wringing, to write to Mr Crawley telling him one of his chaplains would look after the Hogglestock services while the case proceeds. This results in one poor chaplain being briskly sent away from the parish the following Sunday, carrying a letter to the bishop setting out clearly why his lordship has no power to act. When summoned to the palace to explain his letter, Mr Crawley gets enormous pleasure from a conversation in which he utterly crushes the weak bishop in front of his wife. Committed for trial, he then decides to resign his parish, and Mrs Proudie is jubilant, yet still the weak bishop agonizes over sending a chaplain to take Mr Crawley's services. In the end, he is so fraught with indecision that his wife herself instructs the chaplain to go to Hogglestock.

In the whole of English literature, the Bishop of Barchester is one of the finest examples of the weak hen-pecked husband, a man who is his wife's puppet and more than a little afraid of her. She constantly insists on interfering in his work, being present in his room when business is conducted, constantly exploiting his weakness to run the diocese. However, her action in sending the chaplain to Hogglestock following Mr Crawley being sent for trial is her final downfall. It gave rise to a difficult conversation between the unhappy couple as he says: "I do not want to speak to you at all," and continues, "I wish you would go away and leave me." She departs from him in distress, and hours later is found dead, following a severe heart attack. A few days later, this sad, weak and unhappy man sits in prayer, and Trollope comments: "I think he was praying that God might save him from being glad his wife was dead."

It is a fair assumption that Dr Thomas Proudie is not the most distinguished or the most remembered Bishop of Barchester. The kindest thing that can be said are the words of his creator: "If he did not do much active good, he never did any harm."

### The Right Reverend Gerald Avery, Bishop of Clevedon

"Hurry up Gerald! The taxi is at the door. It would never do to be late for the Buck House Garden Party. HMQ might never invite anyone from our order again." Gerald, at that time Archdeacon of South Kensington, drags himself from his letters and papers in the study

and wearily joins Anne, his wife, in the taxi. He smiles
to himself as he recalls her words: "our order"; she is
always Mrs Archdeacon, considering herself as much a
part of the archdeacon's "order" as he is himself. Just the
same, he reflects, HMQ would be unlikely to exclude all
archdeacons from his parties just because one of their
number was late on one occasion.

Anne is "dressed up to the nines", as the old saying
goes. A tasteful simple blue-and-white new summer
dress, gracefully topped by her inherited pearls and a
magnificent broad-brimmed dark-blue straw summer
hat, make her every inch an archdeacon's wife. But she
hasn't finished yet. She is determined that Gerald will
arrive before too long at the top of the ecclesiastical tree;
she has not planned his elevation from mere parish
priest to archdeacon in vain. "Gerald," she says, as the
taxi passes under Admiralty Arch, "several people we
shall meet today could do you good. I'll round them
up. Just come over when I sign you. Don't let me down."

Mrs Avery never tires of her life's work of supporting
her husband by "piloting him towards the purple",
constantly ensuring that the right people are thrown
in his path. At home on the last Friday of every month,
she hosts an early evening drinks party at the spacious
and attractive house which for some years has been
the official residence of the Archdeacon of Kensington.
Living in London, there is always a sprinkling of the
"great and the good" at these occasions along with
local personalities and prominent figures from select

Kensington church congregations and even the odd priest. On one such occasion, Harry Rogers, a local solicitor, had a bet of one pound with his fellow guest Bill Marshall, a headmaster, that as they entered the room together the archdeacon would at that moment be talking to the most important person in it. He won his bet easily as Gerald was seen closeted in a corner in deep conversation with the High Sheriff of Greater London.

Anne Avery never loses an opportunity of promoting her husband's cause, as much for her own ambition as for his future; deep down there is a longing to be Mrs Bishop. Sadly, her efforts are not always rewarded. One day, she had the good fortune to sit next to the Bishop of London at a great feast in the city. Towards the end of the dinner, she said to him, "Bishop, Gerald has been working for you now as archdeacon for over seven years. It's surely time for him to move on and up?" Her reward was a weak smile and silence from the great man. It was an occasion which lingered long in her mind, and it was not a happy memory.

Gerald Avery himself is a deeply ambitious priest, not unappreciative of his wife's support for his cause. He has his own methods of augmenting her strategy. He belongs to a fashionable Pall Mall Club favoured by many senior church figures and politicians, fertile ground for the ongoing work of laying foundations for the future. He also has other carefully nurtured pathways to tread.

Ever since Cambridge, he has enjoyed letter writing and administration, and has used his talents in these areas to the full. From early in his life as a priest, he has been a member of the General Synod, the Church's Parliament, and rarely fails to speak in debates as a way of keeping his name before a useful audience. A few years previously, he had got himself appointed Secretary to a General Synod Working Party on Parish Boundaries, an ongoing project likely to last several years and due to culminate in a major report with appropriate recommendations. The work entailed constant contact with local authorities, government ministers and diocesan offices, as well as offering regular involvement with persons of influence and power. He was assisted in the work by two young personal assistants based in Church House, Westminster, where he was frequently to be found roaming the corridors and conversing with anyone useful he found there.

A few years ago, Avery had struck up a conversation with a church media figure in Church House, and the two had ended up having lunch together in a restaurant nearby. Guy, who ran a small public relations business and advised several dioceses on press and media relations, took a liking to the archdeacon and gave him a small piece of advice that took root: "If you want to move to a more senior office in the Church, there is one thing you have to do. Write a book. It rarely fails." It was complimentary advice from a figure who usually only gave it for a fee. Gerald never forgot the lesson.

Over time, the archdeacon had published many articles on a variety of theological topics in *Theology*

*Today*, a respected Church publication, along with lighter material in the *Church Times* and other publications. He now brought all this material together, added a couple of other pieces on his experience of contemporary church life and published the collection under the catchy title *I was there at the time.* His efforts were rewarded by mixed reviews, although he was saddened by one piece that spoke of a "mixed miscellany of varying quality". However, he had produced a book, and he was more than happy when his meanderings produced several invitations to speak at Church conferences and diocesan "away days" for clergy.

The combined efforts of Anne and Gerald Avery are finally rewarded with success when he is nominated Bishop of Clevedon, a junior bishop in the diocese of Bath and Wells. He is still only 48, and "If I can make Clevedon, I can make Canterbury" is a thought that ever comes to mind. Meanwhile, his faithful spouse rejoices in further scope for her skills in laying foundations for his future.

Sadly, he has discovered there is a dark side to his good wife's concern for his welfare. As archdeacon she had always taken a keen interest in his work, but as Bishop of Clevedon his involvement is with even greater matters. She has gradually become more involved in his daily work and constantly tries to intervene in diocesan affairs. He is aware of becoming more and more "henpecked". It is a development that does not augur well for the future.

# 3

# The Climber

## The Reverend Obadiah Slope

Mr Slope is not a person to whom you warm. Although tall and well made, he has a big mouth, thin bloodless lips, protruding pale brown eyes and a nose that looks spongy and porous. Shaking his hand is never a pleasant experience, as a clammy perspiration always clings to him; he is a damp character with a certain greasiness about his person. To these physical matters could be added a censorious, judgemental nature. Central to his work as a priest is ensuring strict Sabbath observance, and his Low Church evangelical faith gives the impression of being more about keeping Old Testament laws than preaching the New Testament faith and love of Jesus. As he stalks the streets in his black clerical garments, his face wears a judgemental expression and even his eye seems to have an anathema lurking in its corner.

Alongside this general unattractiveness, Mr Slope has a lively interest in filthy lucre. An early understanding with Olivia, a daughter of a London priest, was terminated when he discovered she would not come to him with a substantial dowry, but when her father became Bishop of Barchester—and therefore a man of means—he attempted to revive this relationship. Happily, the lady had more sense. His ambition to pursue and marry Eleanor Bold, the daughter of a prominent Barchester priest, was also inspired by financial motives; this idea only sprang into life when he discovered she had substantial independent means.

He intends to climb high on the ecclesiastical ladder. Consumed with ambition, all the personal gifts he can command are pressed into service in the cause of this primary aim. Skilled both in speech and manner, he can stoop to fawn where necessary or in a moment assume the power of a tyrant if this suits his cause. A powerful preacher, he also has considerable pastoral gifts which are exercised mainly among women, men being more adept in "rumbling" him. Nor is he short of brains; he has published several papers on theological subjects.

Mr Slope's main weapon in climbing the greasy ecclesiastical pole is the use of carefully thought-out strategy. Earlier in life, he had been vicar of a London church where a faithful member of his flock had been a certain Mrs Proudie. He knew her husband was a priest who mixed in the highest metropolitical circles, and he worked out that if in the future Dr Proudie achieved high office it would not be unhelpful to have Mrs Proudie as a close friend. Fortunately, the good lady shared his passion for Sabbath Day observance, and this formed a convenient platform on which to build their relationship. As night follows day, when Dr Proudie became Bishop of Barchester, Obadiah Slope went with him as his chaplain.

He has a vivid memory of sitting in a railway carriage with Bishop and Mrs Proudie, the three of them bound for the bishop's palace at Barchester at the start of Dr Proudie's time there. The "strategy cogs" in the new chaplain's mind were already whirring, planning how he could establish himself at the top of the Barchester tree. He had worked out the bishop was both a weak man and one who would have to spend many weeks of the year in London on church business, two things that would allow Slope, as chaplain, to become de facto bishop of the diocese and hold the purse strings. If Mrs Proudie unfortunately had the same idea, he reflected she too would have to be away with her husband, and if the worst came to the worst, he could always join with the bishop against his wife. By the time the train drew into Barchester station, all was worked out; it was time to start building up a Slope Party among the clergy of the diocese.

Before the new chaplain had been in Barchester long, the Dean of Barchester died, and this desirable post became vacant. Immediately all Mr Slope's considerable powers of strategy were called into action to secure the appointment for himself. He knew the bishop was shortly due to visit the archbishop, and it would be useful if his name could be mentioned favourably at Lambeth Palace in connection with this juicy appointment. When the bishop showed surprise at Mr Slope's interest in such a senior post as well as hesitation about making his journey to London, his chaplain was able to give strong support on both grounds. In strategy, attention to detail is crucial: he made sure the letter confirming the Lambeth engagement was not only written but placed in the post box by his own fair hand.

This much sought-after Barchester appointment affords insight into another aspect of the Slope advancement strategy. He knows the truth of the saying "There's only one thing worse than being mentioned in the newspapers and that's not being mentioned in them." He is careful to make sure that he has friends in the press, and over the years has cultivated Tom Towers, a senior journalist at *The Times* of the day. In this way, Slope makes sure his name is before the public through regular articles on theological topics in the paper; he even entered into controversy with a leading Oxford don in its august columns. Through Towers, he has ensured that the newspaper gives strong editorial support to his hopes of becoming the next Dean of Barchester. Happily, however, his careful and sustained strategy here has gone unrewarded.

Tom Towers is a reminder that Slope's scheming always involves exploiting other people as tools to further his aims. Mrs Proudie and her weak husband are at the heart of much of his plotting, which is not always either kind or honourable. Others also suffer from it. For example, Mr Quiverful, a harassed family man, is vicar of a poor country parish. The chaplain visited him and promised a better endowed appointment, but on a further visit the post was cruelly snatched from him, entirely to serve the chaplain's selfish scheming. On both these occasions Mr Slope used his verbal skills to engage not only in disingenuous explanations but in untrue statements; honesty is frequently a casualty in his conversations. He had earlier used the same technique in his study when, at the instruction of the bishop, he met Mr Harding, another priest, to offer him the post of Warden of Hiram's Hospital, a famous Barchester almshouse. He expertly twisted the terms of the appointment to make it most unattractive, and when Mr Harding expressed the wish to think further before deciding, the chaplain then reported to the bishop—entirely for his own purposes—that the priest had refused it.

The chaplain's ecclesiastical ambitions are destined to remain unfulfilled. Despite elaborate strategy for self-advancement being at the heart of everything he touches, lack of basic common sense is to be his downfall. He constantly takes actions which alienate those around him. A cathedral sermon he preached within days of arriving in Barchester was a highly successful piece of oratory and widely acclaimed, but totally lacking in tact. He "knocked" cathedral worship and the central place music held in it in such a way that the cathedral clergy made plans to ensure he never preached there again. Mrs Proudie, who had given him much support,

could hardly have been expected to continue it when
the chaplain was the cause of her being excluded from
her husband's study. One day the bishop had asked her
to depart from it, saying "My dear, Mr Slope and I are
very busy." From that moment, she determined that the
chaplain would no longer control her husband. Again,
he showed little grace as the bishop, Mrs Proudie and the
master of an Oxford college were in deep conversation
at a garden party by walking up and peremptorily
demanding an introduction to the master.

On a wider front, Slope's general awareness is sadly
lacking. Most of the clergy of the diocese of Barchester
are drawn mainly from the High Church end of the
Church of England, where formality, ceremony and
tradition in worship are central. Mr Slope belongs to the
other extreme, the Low Church evangelical party, and
fails to see that the scales are weighted against him rising
in that diocese. Socially he is also out of his depth; he did
not come from a prosperous or affluent background and
was "a scholarship boy" at his Cambridge college. He
has entered a world of "gentlemen-like clerical doctors",
"comfortable canons" and "well-fed minor canons", where
he seems an intruder. Meeting him for the first time, it
was not surprising that the Archdeacon of Barchester
had immediately proclaimed, "Good Heavens ... did
you ever see any animal less like a gentleman?" or that
the archdeacon's father-in-law, a mild priest if there ever
was one, added, " ... Mr Slope was not gentleman-like
in his manners, of that I am quite sure."

On his arrival in Barchester, the chaplain immediately realized it was this very archdeacon who would become an implacable foe in his strategy of dominating the diocese. It was here his planning showed a massive lack of common sense and no grasp of reality. The idea that a penniless junior priest living in "grace and favour" rooms in the bishop's palace might rule over a wealthy and experienced senior priest holding high office also demonstrated an enormous conceit and arrogance. It was a strategy bound for failure.

In his early days in London, Mr Slope had been a "ladies' man", and his silky whispers had charmed the fair sex. In Barchester, he assumes that after paying court to Eleanor Bold, she and her fortune would fall into his hands. He imagines his quarry to be in love with him, and all that is now needed is to use his verbal dexterity in making an attractive proposal. Again, his lack of common sense shows him rather painfully that he has quite misread the lady. He has great difficulty in getting her to listen to him at all, and when he persists in his approach and touches her person for further effect, his reward is a well-deserved sharp slap on the face.

It is another lady who is the instrument of Mr Slope's final fall from grace. He has spent many hours sitting at the feet of Signora Neroni, adoring the beauty of a strikingly attractive but disabled married lady, now separated from her husband. She often holds court from a couch in her living room, and the chaplain is a regular visitor. News of this habit reaches the palace and finds his former friend and ally Mrs Proudie in no mood to show mercy. The chaplain is summoned into the bishop's presence where she greatly enjoys telling him: "Do you think I have not heard of you kneeling at that creature's feet . . . and of your constant slobbering over her hand?" Minutes later the bishop indicates that the time has come for his chaplain to move on. As a cheque for monies due is promised, it is Mrs Proudie who holds the door open for her former friend to depart.

Mr Slope leaves Barchester with never a backward look. Before long, he is consoling the widow of a rich sugar refiner in London. Soon they are married and installed in a comfortable house in London's Baker Street, where the former chaplain has become the priest at a nearby church. He nobly upholds the traditions of his family, it recorded "the Slopes never starve . . . they live on the fat of the land".

Nevertheless, Mr Slope's literary creator tells us that this priest is not a bad man, despite his way of life appearing to be in total conflict with the faith he teaches. Anthony Trollope writes: "His motives, like those of most men, were mixed. He believed in the religion he taught; harsh, unpalatable and uncharitable as that religion was. He believed those he wished under his hoof to be the enemies of that religion . . . he taught himself to think that in doing much for the protection of his own interests he was also doing much for the promotion of religion."

## The Reverend Adrian Booth

Casting an eye round the living room in a Bristol flat late one afternoon your eye would meet a typical scene. Unwashed coffee cups, a discarded wine bottle on the mantelpiece, books and papers littered on the chairs and floor, an open laptop on a table. Lounging amid the detritus of student life are Graham and Martin, two of the three occupants of the flat, along with their current girlfriends, Sally and Jean. All four are students in the English Department at Bristol University.

"Old Prof. Edwards is giving a lecture on Keats on Zoom in a few minutes, but I'm not in the mood today—anyway, his script will be sent round before long. We can read it then. Let's open another bottle before we go out to eat." The sentiment seems to meet with general approval. Four glasses are happily filled and the gossip session that has been in progress resumed with renewed vigour. "Where's Adrian this afternoon?" asks one of the party. Graham responds, "He's gone out for the day with Mary—won't be back until later." Martin comments, "You can read him like a book. Mary's father is a bishop, and Adrian is going to train as a priest next year. She's also got a bit of dosh, because her father is not a poor man. Adrian knows what he's doing trying to net Mary. Good luck to him."

Sally says: "Adrian is one of the Prof's favourites in our year, and he's up for President of the University Debating Society next term. I'm not sure how he does it. He just seems to have the knack of coming out on top." After a minute, she adds: "*War and Peace* is one of our set books. Adrian reminds me of one of the people there, Prince Vasily. Hang on. It's on your bookshelf." With that Sally gets up and opens the massive volume and still standing up reads the following words with dramatic effect:

> Prince Vasily was not given to planning ahead. ... various plans and considerations were always forming in his mind, according to circumstances and individual encounters, but he was never fully conscious of them, even though they were his main interest in life ... He never said to himself, for instance "Here is a man with power. I must gain his friendship and confidence, and use him to gain a grant from some special fund", nor did he say "Now that Pierre is a wealthy man, I must hoodwink him into marrying my daughter and lending me the forty thousand I need." But when ever he came across a man of power he knew instinctively whether this man might be of some use, and Prince Vasily would ingratiate himself and take the first opportunity—again instinctively and without any forethought—to flatter him, get on familiar terms with him and then tell him what he wanted.

"Don't you think there's a touch of all that in Adrian? He just knows how to get on the right side of people and what's good for him. Perhaps he doesn't even know that's why he's chasing Mary? I hope she works out his sordid little scheme and drops him." There follows vigorous discussion on the absent couple, ending in general agreement that if Adrian loves Mary, and she returns his love, what did it matter?

Eight years later, Graham and Martin meet for a lunch in the city of London where Graham works in a merchant bank; Martin has walked over from his chambers in the Temple where he is a junior barrister. The conversation ranges far and wide and goes back to the old Bristol days. "What happened to our friend Adrian?" wonders Martin. "Did he ever become a priest?"

"Oh, yes," responds Graham. "Jean is a teacher in Oxford, and I see her sometimes. She says that Adrian and Mary live not very far away from her. Her father the bishop arranged a smart curacy for him in a central London parish, and now he's senior chaplain to the Bishop of Oxford, and as busy making friends all round him as he ever was. Some people never change."

# 4

# The Saint

## The Reverend Septimus Harding

Entering Barchester Cathedral by the south door, you might bump into a kind comfortable-looking genial priest of mature years who is just coming out. He greets you with a warm smile, holding the door open, and with a cheerful voice says "Good morning. Enjoy your visit."

This is Septimus Harding, the cathedral precentor, the priest who is in charge of the cathedral's music and choir. Your brief meeting brings to mind those memorable words of St Paul "Whatever is true, whatever is pure, whatever is lovely, whatever is gracious . . . think on those things." You reflect that here is a priest who seems the very embodiment of them.

Children can make unconscious judgements on people. They love to respond joyfully to the open, kind person "comfortable in their own skin" but hold back from others, led on by a kind of "sixth sense". Children are always happy to be with Septimus Harding, and sometimes he carries "in his pocket sundry treasures with which he had come prepared to delight" them.

At the end of life, his constant companion was Susan, a grandchild, who he called Posy, and with whom he spent many happy hours talking and playing cat's cradle. It is as if the honesty and innocence of a child recognizes these same qualities in others.

Alongside the world of cathedral music, Harding is Warden of Hiram's Hospital, an almshouse for 12 retired wool workers from Barchester, founded as a charity in the fifteenth century by John Hiram. Here he lives with his as yet unmarried daughter Eleanor in a comfortable spacious warden's house set in a delightful garden by a river. Nothing could be more comfortable. His home is a constant delight, snug with his books, his beloved 'cello and his music. His "old men" adore him and he them. As soon as the warden discovered there was sufficient money available, he immediately gave his charges an increase in their pensions. Even after retiring from the wardenship, he loves returning to pass the time of day with them.

Sadly, it was this very increase in the resources of the Hiram Trust which has led to the warden's painful retirement. By Victorian times, the value of the original Trust funds has greatly increased, and John Bold, a local Barchester campaigner on church matters, draws Mr Harding's attention to the generous stipend he is now receiving, contrasted with the meagre stipend given to his resident pensioners. Bold went on to make the Barchester matter a national concern, causing *The Times* of the day to highlight this issue which faced all ancient charities of that time.

It is easy to imagine how this searchlight of publicity disturbs the peace and calm of the warden's life and how his good, sensitive and delicate nature begins to question his position. He becomes miserable and ill at ease. "Was his humble name to be bandied about in men's mouths, as the gormandizer of the resources of the poor, as one who had filched from the charity of other ages wealth which had been intended to relieve the old and infirm? Was he to be gibbeted by the press, to become a byword for oppression, to be named as an example of the greed of the English Church?" He is even more disturbed when some of his resident pensioners begin to mutter that more of the Hiram money is due to them.

The irony of this situation is that no one could be less concerned about money than Septimus Harding. It is common knowledge that "no man lived less addicted to filthy lucre than the Warden". He is on record as saying: "Money is worth thinking of, but it is not worth very much thought." Against this background, the outcome is inevitable. Such a good and noble spirit could not rest until the burden is shed and the wardenship laid down.

Sir Abraham Haphazard QC, the lawyer engaged by the bishop to deal with Bold, has to be told of this decision, and so Harding has to go to London. There is a certain wry amusement as this gentle spirit arrives in the big city after being closeted for so long in Barchester's provincial backwater. He kills time in Westminster Abbey, where he observes things are not as well ordered as in Barchester, and is later served with a chop and potatoes by an untidy girl in a London chop house that was "rough and dirty and disreputable" and where everything seems to him to be impregnated with fish. He then goes into the new world of a cigar divan shop in the Strand and is offered sherbet or coffee and a cigar. He has a feeling sherbet should be drunk sitting cross-legged and so opts for coffee and gives the proffered cigar to a waiter. After a refreshing sleep on one of the divans, he moves on to Lincoln's Inn for his decisive late-night meeting with Sir Abraham, who listens to the warden with astonishment. The lawyer is a man of the world and, we are told: "This poor little clergyman, cowed into such an act of extreme weakness by a newspaper article, was to Sir Abraham so contemptible an object, that he hardly knew how to talk to him as a rational being."

Leaving his beloved wardenship is a wrench and an agony, but he is able to continue as cathedral precentor and alongside this post becomes vicar of the small "light duty" St Cuthbert's church in Barchester. A look at the dealings Mr Harding has with those around him sheds further light on the sheer goodness of this remarkable man.

His closest relationship is with Eleanor, his younger daughter, who has lived with him at the hospital, his "Nelly". One night as "she sat on his knee, as she sometimes would in their gayest mood, and with her arm around his neck", she prevails upon him to share his worries about the hospital and has no hesitation in encouraging him to resign. "Give it up, papa", she counsels, and there can be no doubt it is her encouragement which pushes him over the edge. Anxiety about how leaving his home will affect his beloved daughter has hurt him more than anything else. His resolve has been strengthened by her words, and he is greatly helped by the comfort she gives him in the days following. Despite being on record as saying lodgings were "not quite respectable", on leaving his spacious beloved warden's house, Harding takes rooms over a chemist's shop in the high street, and Eleanor follows him, squeezing into a small back bedroom.

For some time while at the hospital, the warden has noted Eleanor's close relationship with John Bold, the campaigner who has drawn national attention to the finances of the hospital and who has become the source of all his problems. As a young boy, Bold, the son of a local doctor, played with Eleanor in the hospital gardens, and she was close both to him and his sister, Mary. This kind and caring man, ascertaining from his daughter that she is indeed in love with Bold, instead of being angry and annoyed, simply encourages her. When he has a party for close friends, he generously invites Bold and we learn that "the Warden declared that Bold was no enemy of his, and encouraged her love". He thought Bold "had all those qualities which are likely to touch a girl's heart. He is brave, he is eager, and amusing;

well-made and good looking; young and enterprising; his character is in all respects good."

Eleanor duly marries but sadly, after a son is born, Bold dies, and she is left on her own, sharing her house with Mary. She makes every effort to encourage her father to leave his lodgings and move in with her, but he resists, motivated by the typically generous thought that one day she might marry again. Earlier, Harding had presented Eleanor with a carriage and two ponies to draw it, an action his son-in-law, the archdeacon, described as "foolishly indulgent".

There is a touch of innocence about Eleanor—perhaps inherited from her father—which is to give him much worry and anxiety. He knows the scheming Mr Slope, the bishop's chaplain, has taken to visiting her from time to time, ostensibly to pave the way for him to return to the hospital, and now there are plans to start a Sunday school at the hospital. Eleanor has innocently offered to become a teacher at it, and Harding has to counsel his daughter: "If I were you, I'm not quite sure I would select Mr. Slope for my guide." Both his son-in-law, the archdeacon, and his wife Susan, Harding's eldest daughter, are most suspicious of Slope's apparent friendship with Eleanor and Slope's visits to her. One day, when Harding is staying with them at Plumstead Rectory, Mrs Grantly tells him of their unhappiness about the matter. Harding replies: "But you don't really mean to say that you suppose Eleanor had ever thought of marrying Mr. Slope? Why, Mr. Bold has only been dead a year." For some time, there is much speculation on the matter both at Plumstead and at those lodgings over the chemist's shop, later fuelled by a long letter from Mr Slope to Eleanor at a time when both she and her father are staying at Plumstead. Harding's generosity and love for his daughter are both expressed in his thoughts at this time: " . . . if she should choose to become Mrs Slope, he had nothing he could justly urge against her doing so. . . . he . . . could not say that she would disgrace herself by marrying a clergyman who stood so well before the world as Mr. Slope did . . . he must get over his aversion as best he might, anything to him would be preferable to the loss of his daughter." The sheer relief and joy that envelops this good man can only be imagined when he finally hears from Eleanor's own lips at a garden party that she has never had the slightest intention of marrying Slope.

A particularly significant figure in Harding's daily life is his son-in-law, the Archdeacon of Barchester, Theophilus Grantly Both Grantly and Harding belong to the same conservative traditional High Church party, as contrasted with the evangelical Low Church party, led largely by Mrs Proudie, the bishop's wife, and Mr Slope, the bishop's chaplain. Yet in other crucial ways the two men could not have been more different from each other. Grantly views Harding as lacking in "push", a man who has spent all his life "lingering on", while the mild precentor is afraid of the archdeacon's assertive personality and unbounded self-confidence. Knowing the archdeacon strongly disapproves of his thoughts of resignation, his visit to London to see Sir Abraham is carried out in secret, using his "modest powers of intrigue" and in constant fear that the archdeacon will stop him if he is discovered.

The archdeacon is utterly in command of his own life and affairs, happy to think he is lord of all he surveys. In contrast, Harding is utterly dependent on his son-in-law. At the end of his life, he recalls: "For authority and guidance and wisdom, and for information as to what was going on in the world, he still turned to his son-in-law the archdeacon—as he had done for the last forty years." It is the archdeacon who controls the precentor's purse strings, who finances his excess spending on his musical interests and who has insured his life for £3,000. Little wonder the precentor is afraid of him.

The two men have contrasting views on people. The archdeacon sees John Bold, the originator of Harding's problems, as "the most vulgar young person I have ever met", regarding him as a pestilent nuisance and a thorn in the flesh, feeling the warden is "imprudent" even to receive him into his house. The charitable and humble Harding simply sees him as a local young boy who used to play in the garden of the warden's house, who holds a view on Hiram's charity he is perfectly entitled to hold and who seems to be falling in love with his daughter Eleanor, which again he is perfectly entitled to do. Both men have regular dealings with Obadiah Slope, the bishop's chaplain, and both find him a pain in the flesh.

While the archdeacon rages and storms, calling him an impudent scoundrel and worse, Harding mildly says: "I don't think I shall ever like that Mr. Slope." Perhaps their biggest difference arises when the old men at the hospital, hearing there could be more money about, get up a petition for increased pensions. The archdeacon is furious and rushes down to the hospital to address the residents in no uncertain tone, while the warden simply says "But, why shouldn't they petition, doctor?", saying he would much rather keep things quiet. "Quiet," said the archdeacon, still speaking with his brazen trumpet, "do you wish to be ruined in quiet?" The warden replies with his touch of customary gentle humour: "Why, if I am to be ruined, certainly." A quiet sense of humour is always bubbling below the surface, and on another occasion, we hear he "brought forth little quiet jokes from the inmost mirth of his heart".

The precentor's gentle spirit is continually tested to the full by his encounters with Mr Slope, and in the early days of their relationship, the chaplain's confident and assured manner causes him a good deal of self-doubt. Soon after his arrival in Barchester, he had interviewed the precentor over the hospital, falsely giving him to understand that the bishop was reshaping the wardenship of the hospital in such a way as to make it difficult for him to return, and paving the way for him to refuse the appointment. Slope told him the world was changing; now there was new work for new men, with the useless rubbish of past ages being carted away and where "work is now required from every man who receives wages". The precentor went away and found himself wanting. Had he been receiving wages and doing little work? "Alas, Alas, the evidence generally seemed to go against him." Was he part of the rubbish to be carted away? Later, when Mr Slope preached a powerful sermon in the cathedral against his style of worship he asked himself again: was he in error? "Surely, he could not have been wrong all his life in chanting the liturgy as he had done?" This good and holy man was uncertain and unsure, questioning himself in a way that would never have occurred to others with greater self-confidence. Happily, on reflection he realizes Mr Slope is not a tutor from whom he wishes to learn and mildly tells Eleanor: "It would be very wicked of me to speak evil of him, for to tell the truth I know no evil of him; but I am not quite sure he is honest. That he is not gentleman-like in his manners, of that I am quite sure."

One of Harding's great comforts in life is his deep friendship with the gentle and much-loved Bishop of Barchester, and he spends many hours at the palace talking with him. They both "loved each other warmly ... they were all in all to each other", and it was to the bishop that Harding first goes to share all his anxiety over the problems of the hospital. Their friendship dates back to the time when Harding had only been a minor canon at the cathedral; they have grown old together, and their relationship throws into relief the precentor's warm and gracious character. "There was a gentleness about the bishop to which the soft womanly affection of Mr Harding particularly endeared itself, and it was quaint to see how these two mild old priests pressed each other's hands, and smiled and made little signs of love." It was never the precentor's way to criticize his bishop, but when his friend Dr Grantly was succeeded by Bishop Proudie, it is recorded that "Never a word did he say against Bishop Proudie . . . but the many words he did say in praise of Bishop Grantly—who, by his showing was surely one of the best churchmen who ever walked through this vale of sorrow—were as eloquent in the dispraise of the existing prelate as could have been more clearly pointed phrases."

Every relationship in Septimus Harding's life speaks of pure goodness. When another priest, Josiah Crawley, is falsely accused of stealing money, the precentor never for one moment believes he is guilty; in his view no priest could ever do such a thing. When it finally becomes clear that he is not to return as warden of the hospital and the appointment is to go to Quiverful, the parish priest of Puddingdale with a large family to support, Harding strongly supports the appointment. He feels the new man's needs are far greater than his own; he shows boundless generosity and insists on going with the new warden to the hospital to commend him to the residents.

Yet despite all his quiet goodness Harding can be surprisingly decisive when necessary. Not only does he resign the wardenship, but he had earlier strongly opposed a potential new resident put forward by the archdeacon in favour of one of his own, more suitable, nominations. He rejects every suggestion made by the bishop for his future, either by moving to the parish made vacant by Quiverful or becoming the bishop's assistant chaplain and companion, drinking wine with him and poking the fire when needed. Most significant of all, when he is later offered the post of Dean of Barchester he declines the appointment, again strongly opposed by the archdeacon. He knows himself well, and feels he is too old and not a sufficiently forceful personality for the role. He follows up this major decision by suggesting his own daughter's fiancé, Francis Arabin, Vicar of St Ewold's, should become dean in his place, a suggestion that bears fruit. Here is not just a good man, but one "with his feet on the ground".

Eleanor becomes chatelaine of the deanery, and her father accepts an invitation to live with her there in his declining years, every day tottering over to the cathedral next door to say his prayers. Generous to the end, on his death bed he suggests that Crawley, now proved innocent of theft, should move to the parish of St Ewold's, a more comfortable berth for him than his present parish and one at that time held by Harding himself.

It is peacefully in his bed at the deanery that Harding takes leave of the world, saying: "I have nothing to regret, nothing to make me unhappy. I know how poor and weak has been my life; but I know how rich and strong is that other life ... why should anyone weep for those who go away full of years—and full of hope?"

Here is a man of generosity, love, courtesy, kindness and truth, who never spoke a harsh or hard word to the end of his life. Trollope's writings are full of those who are or who are not gentlemen, but he never defines what goes into making a gentleman. Septimus Harding is perhaps his walking definition of the word.

## The Reverend David Ward

Born into a middle-class home in North London, David Ward's father had wanted him to go into a solicitor's office and train as a lawyer. However, the family has always been deeply involved in their local parish church, and David told his father he would like to spend his life as a priest. The idea did not go down well, and he was told, "You will be poor for the rest of your days, and you have always liked a comfortable life." Yet the boy would not be shaken, telling his father he had himself to blame for bringing him up to go to church. David decided not to go to a university but instead became a student at a church college run by Church of England monks. Five years later, he became a priest, serving as a curate in Manchester and then becoming Vicar of Walton, a small market town in Yorkshire.

Now in his late fifties, David has been Vicar of Walton for nearly 30 years. He never married and will tell you that as a student he had several girlfriends, but none "clicked" and he never fell in love. He slowly began to realize his role in life was to dedicate it to undivided attention to his service as a priest, a destiny he has never regretted and which has brought him inner peace and composure. A short, stocky man, his bright eyes twinkle with goodwill and he seems to be one of those fortunate even-tempered people, always with a kind smile on his face. He is not a scholar or learned man but profound and wise in his dealings with people. David lives in the rambling Victorian vicarage next to the church, shared with an old lady who is his housekeeper, a dog, two cats and several constantly changing student lodgers. One of the rooms serves as his book-lined study and houses his old battered grand piano, a room that speaks of both comfort and chaos.

David Ward has seen much change in Walton since he arrived. Several housing estates have grown up on the edge of the town, and the population has nearly doubled, while transport links with Leeds, the nearest big city, have not increased to meet demand. The high street now mainly consists of building societies and charity shops while most young people leave the town to find work elsewhere. David and the church building—a Victorian structure of no special merit—are the only things that seem to have remained constant in recent years.

Joe keeps the local garage and says: "Our vicar David is doing okay", which in Yorkshire-speak means he's a good man. He has baptized, married and buried many of the population and is now baptizing and marrying their children. A lot of the girls have moved away but return to Walton as young women to get married by him. Many folk in the town see him as a shoulder on which to lean—a sort of male agony aunt—and when problems come it has become a common saying in Walton "It's time for a little talk with David." His time is divided equally between visiting his flock in their homes, the Black Bull, the pub next to the church where he has many friends, and the local hospital. He often laughs about the time at the hospital when an elderly lady in the bed said to him, "You don't seem at all like a vicar." Did she simply mean he seemed unexpectedly human, or did she mean there was nothing spiritual about him?

The bishop has tried several times to tempt David away from Walton. A few years ago, he was asked to join the staff of a college training priests and to share with them his wide experience of parish work. He took the view he would rather continue doing the work than just talking about it, and in any case, it was the simple fact he had stayed so long in one place that gave value to his work. On another occasion, the bishop offered him a bigger church in Leeds, but he was not tempted. David often says the real reason the bishop wanted him to move was so that the vicarage could be sold, and a new vicar put in a smaller place on a housing estate. Several new houses could also then be built in the garden and a tidy sum produced to smooth over the financial problems of the diocese.

One of his pet hates is the amount of paper that comes through the door from the Church of England, most of which lands swiftly in the wastepaper basket. He refuses to fill in questionnaires, thinks the Church spends far too much money on bureaucracy, and wonders why it employs so many people in offices. "There's a shortage of priests," he says, "but 60 lay people at desks in the Diocesan Office. Something wrong somewhere."

When occasion demands, David can be a mild "ideas" man. He recalls how, in a busy week, he booked a baptism at the main Sunday worship, when the family involved were leading lights in town life, but had quite forgotten that earlier he had also booked a civic service for the same time, which the mayor and council of Walton were due to attend. Crisis! Neither arrangement could be changed without major problems, but David suddenly remembered that the town council had recently given some money to repair the font. He quickly arranged for the archdeacon to come and preach at this service and made quite sure his special visitor started the sermon by saying, "I am so glad to accept the vicar's invitation to preach at this special service, when Baby Jane's baptism has been arranged. It takes place on the first occasion the font is used after its recent restoration and when the mayor and council are present. This is a most appropriate occasion to thank the mayor and council for their generous gift." All parties went home pleased, and David breathed again.

David is a deeply sensitive man and a gifted pianist. A few years ago, after much blood, sweat and tears, and many jumble sales, enough cash had been raised to repair the dilapidated church organ. The organist, Peter Howells, came over to the vicarage to talk about the service at which the organ was to be dedicated. Peter suggested that the occasion should begin with a rousing hymn of praise, when the organ could be heard at its best. David thought for a moment and then said, "No, I've got a better idea. Let's start the service quietly and sing the first couple of hymns without any accompaniment. Then when we come to the dedication part, and after some prayers I will say, 'Let the organ sound', and you will come in with some mighty crashing chords." The occasion is still remembered in Walton as a memory to be treasured, when a shiver went down the many spines of those present.

Walton's vicar is a gentle and kind man, but a shade too trusting. As a curate years ago, he once received a letter on the bishop's writing paper summoning him to meet the bishop for a disciplinary talk at 9 a.m. the following Monday. He was greatly distressed and preparing to obey the summons, when his vicar and boss phoned him to say that it was simply a hoax cooked up by his fellow curates. He suffered much and was not amused. On another occasion, after he had been at Walton for a few years, he was asked to go and say prayers in a house said to be haunted and where it was claimed there was "an evil presence". Acting in trust, he did so, only to discover later it was a ruse by the wily occupants to convince the council their house was haunted, to get a rent reduction.

David Ward is a good man. As long as the Church of England has a few like him, it won't go far wrong.

# 5

# The Man of Power

## The Venerable Theophilus Grantly, Archdeacon of Barchester

Archdeacon Grantly once pronounced: "A round dinner table is the most abominable article of furniture ever invented." It spoke to him of something "democratic and parvenu", an item lacking in gentility, usually of common oak rather than mahogany, made to shine by constant polishing. What he did not say was that he loved a long table with guests seated on either side with himself at the head.

An archdeacon is an ecclesiastical chief executive, the powerful figure at the business end of a diocese where the bishop is the chairman, a little removed from the ground-floor scene of action. Grantly is wedded to being at the head of the table and wielded unfettered power while his father was Bishop of Barchester. He stalked the parishes instilling awe into all who met him, a striking figure of authority in his clerical shovel hat, shiny black gaiters and black clerical gloves. Here was a priest whose sheer grandeur struck awe into the hearts of those who met him, decorous and opulent, never putting aside the demeanour that became him as a man of authority.

The archdeacon knew all about churches and vicarages, their fabric and their occupants, and exercised his power wisely. Always concerned that a new priest should be both "up to the job" and personally compatible with his parishioners, he often consulted his clergy on appointments. He enjoyed frequent socializing with his colleagues, and we see him in convivial spirit educating his brother priests on the issues of the day as he drank and played cards with them. Grantly ruled over his neighbours for many years and never became unpopular so that "it may be presumed he had exercised some wisdom".

Sadly, all good things come to an end. The archdeacon's power is drastically curbed by the death of his father and the arrival of a new regime. The new man, Bishop Proudie, cuts a weak and spineless figure and has little character or presence. Grantly has no respect for him. The bishop is largely run by his strong and determined wife, the renowned Mrs Proudie, aided and abetted by Obadiah Slope, her husband's chaplain—a man also intoxicated with power and equally ambitious to be *de facto* bishop. It is not a pretty picture, and the archdeacon is determined to oppose the new regime with every weapon at his disposal. War is declared on the bishop's palace and all its occupants, although it is a war that Grantly keeps in balance, never allowing it to dominate his life. When Mrs Grantly tells him that Mrs

Proudie has died suddenly, he simply says : "She was an uncomfortable woman—so uncomfortable I can't believe anyone will regret her. Dear me! Only to think she's gone! You may as well give me my tea."

This conflict also has a spiritual dimension. Mrs Proudie and Mr Slope are Low Church evangelicals, wedded to simplicity in worship and a puritan style of life. This is not to the archdeacon's taste. He and the majority of the Barchester clergy come from the High Church party, marked by traditional rites of worship, formality and emphasis on the strong links binding Church and State. The division between the two is so deep that when Grantly is angry, he sometimes finds that when he comes to say his prayers at night, he "would hardly be able to survive the ordeal".

The record of the archdeacon's authority and influence is long. Two incidents are especially memorable. In the first, he arrives at Hiram's Hospital, a home for elderly male pensioners, to be told that the residents are about to present a petition to the bishop for an increased pension. His swift reactions show power at work. He initially suggests letting the petition go ahead and then destroying it, or alternatively taking it up to the bishop's palace, where he would write a firm negative response and then get the bishop to sign it. Both courses illustrate all too well he was "too fond of his own way and not sufficiently scrupulous in his manner of obtaining it". The upright warden of the hospital was unhappy with both approaches, so Grantly takes immediate swift action. Over the warden's head, he rings the hospital bell to summon the residents to an immediate meeting in the grounds, taking care to ensure that the warden, who has endeavoured to escape the ordeal, remains present. Like all men of power, Grantly knows that division in the camp can be fatal.

The frail pensioners gather outside, dominated by this fine figure of authority, kitted out in the full grandeur of his office. Instinctively the archdeacon knows that the visual aspect of power will not be lost on his hearers—although he might not have been pleased to learn his nickname was "Calves", a reference to his finely gaitered legs. He had not expected to make a speech when he had entered the hospital, but his enormous self-confidence and dexterity with words, which so often go with power, ensure a brilliant "off-the-cuff" performance. Here is no velvet glove as he begins, "Now, my men, I want to say a few words to you." There follows an insulting tirade in which he addresses his hearers as "worn out and ungrateful old men", who needed assuring that when John Hiram founded the hospital, he had not intended its residents to be prosperous citizens. The archdeacon took the view that the lower orders should be grateful for what is done for them and should not rise up and ask for more; that way leads to revolution, and the petition has to be nipped in the bud. Then as now, power exploited class and status.

The second incident occurs some years later. The saintly Septimus Harding, the archdeacon's father-in-law, had been a much loved and respected warden of Hiram's Hospital. Earlier, he had resigned the post on a matter of principle and had received a letter from the archbishop congratulating him on his stand. Now he has been offered the tempting and prestigious post of Dean of Barchester, probably a delayed reward. Grantly is delighted at the prospect of seeing a member of his family in such a senior position, particularly because this will mean a major set-back for Mr Slope. Not only had the chaplain hoped for the post himself, but the archdeacon's own power will be strengthened in his internecine war with the palace. When over dinner he is told by Mr Harding that he intends to reject this tempting promotion, "the decanter almost falls from the archdeacon's hand" in utter amazement. He cannot believe what he regards as utter stupidity and quickly brushes aside Mr Harding's objections that at his age he needs peace and rest, and that anyway the duties are beyond him.

One of Grantley's principal points to his father-in-law over the deanery offer concerns money; he argues that it is nonsense for a priest of low rank and £200 p.a. to refuse appointment to a higher rank at £1,200 p.a. Money and power frequently walk together and the archdeacon's life affords a prime example. He believes "money speaks", and it gives a firm foundation for his power and influence in the diocese. His father, the late bishop, had left him great wealth, and in his dispute with the present bishop, it comforts him to feel that he could have bought every individual possession of the present bishop's family "and restored it to them as a gift without feeling much loss". His stable is well stocked with fast horses and carriages; he had a whole string of curates, and at Plumstead Rectory "the tea consumed was the very best, the coffee the very blackest, and the cream the very thickest". In addition to the rectory land, he also owns an extensive adjacent estate and is in effect both rector and squire.

The archdeacon is "fond of obtaining money", taking the view "If honest men did not squabble for money in this wicked world of ours the dishonest men would get it all." It was in character that he had earlier advised his father-in-law to keep the whole of his stipend as warden of Hiram's Hospital, even when the national press was raising convincing arguments that it was excessive. He not only uses money as a lever of power with the bishop but even with members of his own family, threatening to change his will and cancel his son Henry's inheritance if he does not withdraw from a marriage of which the archdeacon at that time disapproved.

Behind many a powerful man lurks a sane and sensible wife. Susan, his trusted helpmate, frequently gives him wise counsel that results in an alteration to Grantley's projected actions. Trollope occasionally gives us a glance of the two as they nestle "in that sacred recess formed by the clerical bed-curtains". The lofty figure that inspires awe and reverence as he strides down the high street of Barchester in his fine hat and clerical garb cuts quite a different picture in his tasselled nightcap and bed attire, stretching himself beneath the bed clothes or yawning as he buries his face in the pillow. It is in the quiet of the bedchamber that the man of power who gives advice to others often receives it himself.

Power, like all gifts and talents, can be misused. Dr Grantly's skill with words is one of his greatest weapons to describe other people whom he disliked. John Bold, a campaigning reformer, is "vulgar" and "a pestilent interfering upstart"; Mr Slope, the loathed bishop's chaplain, is "filth" and "a fellow raked up from the gutters of Marylebone". The bishop's wife is "impertinent" and a "She-Beelzebub". He is a colourful figure, and such comments are usually accompanied by his trademark words "Good Heavens" along with a sneer. The archdeacon is an expert sneerer.

His quick tongue can also be used in an unfortunate way. Asked by Mrs Proudie, a keen advocate of Sunday schools, whether there was one in his parish he replied "Sabbath Day Schools ... upon my word, I can't tell ... there's none at Plumstead", which he knew was a downright lie. Hearing Mr Slope declare strongly against the intoning or singing of prayers in church, he responds that he might decide to "procure the co-operation of any number of gentleman-like-curates well trained in the mystery of doing so". In the drawing room of the bishop's palace, where he once lived with his father, he declares to his hostess: "Dear, dear ... how many rubbers of whist I have played in this room", well knowing that card games are an anathema to its present evangelical occupants. Such childish comments are unworthy of him.

The Victorian Church was felt by many to be in need of "root and branch" reform, but Dr Grantly remains a strong traditionalist and battles against any moves that might lead to change. In particular, his encouragement to his father-in-law to continue taking his full stipend as warden of Hiram's Hospital is given in the face of constant press claims that the system paying this stipend was in urgent need of reform. Given his way, the archdeacon would disband every committee and commission that would even dare to ask a question about church revenues and is "always ready to take up the cudgels against all comers on behalf of the Church Militant". The observer is left with the shrewd suspicion that the archdeacon is against reform because he suspects his power might thereby be limited; preserving the status quo holds no dangers for him.

Like many men addicted to power, he is a social snob. He loves going up to London to visit Charles, his eldest son, married to Lady Anne, where he meets the men "he loved to meet". He is intensely proud that his daughter, Lady Griselda, is married to a Marquis, but rarely goes to stay with them because he does not care to stay in any house where "those around him were supposed to be bigger than himself". Accustomed to live on terms of equality with the gentry, the idea that his son Henry might marry the daughter of a poverty-stricken fellow priest accused of theft appals him. He comments that such a marriage would "kill me".

Dr Grantly may have enjoyed exercising power, but on many matters he is forced into a series of "U" turns. Before Eleanor, his sister-in-law, married John Bold he had roundly abused her future husband and tried to stop the marriage, but in later years the two men become good friends. When Bold died, the archdeacon suspected Eleanor was planning to become engaged to his bitter enemy, Mr Slope. He could not have been more wrong. His suspicion that a fellow priest, Josiah Crawley, was a thief proved false, while he had to withdraw his strong opposition to Henry, his son, marrying Crawley's daughter. Later, Septimus Harding's decisions to resign the wardenship of Hiram's Hospital and then to decline the offer of the deanery, both things opposed by the archdeacon, were seen by him afterwards to be wise.

Behind this love of power lies a family man with a loving wife, five children and a happy and comfortable home. Convivial by nature, he is fond of dinner parties with the local squirarchy and "modest claret jugs" and hates the parson who won't fill up his glass after dinner. On quiet evenings, he is not above locking his study door to take a naughty French novel out of a locked drawer. "Keenly susceptible to the influence of feminine charms", emotionally he is also very sensitive. As he stands beside his dying father's bedside, hoping he might succeed him as bishop, we see "this proud worldly man" sinking to his knees, praying his sins might be forgiven him. There are tears in his eyes as he hears of the engagement of Eleanor and his friend Francis Arabin. Great depth of personal feeling lies beneath the power.

The last word must be with Trollope, his creator, who tells us the archdeacon "upholds propriety of conduct both by word and precept. He is generous to the poor and hospitable to the rich; in matters of religion, he is sincere, and yet no Pharisee; he is in earnest, but no fanatic. On the whole the Archdeacon of Barchester is a man doing more good than harm—a man to be furthered and supported, yet perhaps also to be controlled."

### The Venerable Frederick Nicholas Anthony Roberts

Frederick Roberts is a child of the vicarage. Educated at a minor public school in the Midlands, he graduated from York University and went straight to a church college in Cambridge to train as a priest, following in his father's footsteps. He completed a short curacy in Birmingham and came to the Lichfield diocese as archdeacon after a long spell as vicar of a large suburban parish on the outskirts of London. All who know him would say that his character has been unmistakably shaped by the appointment he held after his curacy and before his time in London, when he emerged from the Royal Anglian Regiment as Captain The Reverend Frederick Roberts MC. He greatly enjoyed his 12 years as an army chaplain, serving in a variety of postings at home and abroad, being awarded the MC for his part in rescuing the crew of a burning tank during the opening months of the Iraq War; not an experience given to many priests.

The archdeacon lives with his wife Louise in a large Georgian house in Lichfield Cathedral Close. They have made it into a gracious and charming home, filled with the kind of brown antique furniture now so much out of fashion, and they live well. Frederick Roberts is not a poor man and is fond of money; there was an unfounded rumour that he only became an army chaplain because the stipend was much higher than that of a parish priest. His father had enjoyed independent means alongside his priest's stipend, and when he died, his substantial investments came to his son, whose own stipend as an archdeacon is a generous one anyway. He also enjoys a small pension from his army days. There are two boys of the marriage, James and Simon, and at holiday times they with their wives and the archdeacon's five grandchildren make the archdeaconry, as the house is known, ring with life and fun.

Archdeacon Roberts is not a man with many hobbies; his main interest is the Church and its affairs. He is a great newspaper addict; occasionally neighbours come in for bridge parties and happily the tennis court in the archdeaconry back garden makes for easy enjoyment of his one sporting addiction and is in use most of the year round. He and Louise frequently dine out with friends and have regular dinner parties themselves, although the choice of his dinner guests is finely controlled. The

house is regularly filled with the great and good of
Lichfield society along with senior Church figures and
their wives. The archdeacon is proud of his position and
laments the fact that archdeacons no longer wear gaiters.
He has always been something of a social snob, and
during his time in the Army developed a delicate nose
for rank and the respect due to it. Unconsciously he now
divides everyone he meets into officers and other ranks.

Much of his time is spent in visiting the parishes
in the archdeaconry, and his flock know when he has
arrived. A tall man, he has a mass of black curly hair
and an upright military stance. Highly polished shoes,
a dark suit and black shirt, topped by his clerical collar
complete the picture—he has no time for modern
clerical shirts in grey or blue. His face is large with a firm
chin, a big mouth, eyes that seem to pierce and a deep
voice which would wake the dead. The clergy know all
too well that a figure has arrived with which they must
reckon. The weaker brethren become apprehensive
when his car sweeps up the vicarage drive, while the
stronger look forward to some stimulating if demanding
talk. Yet weak and strong alike know that underneath
this commanding figure lies a heart of gold. If a priest is
laid low by illness, it is not unknown for the archdeacon
to appear and cover his duties, and he is known to be
a wise counsellor when parish, family or financial
problems rear their ugly head.

Frederick Roberts is an accomplished preacher,
incapable of producing a dull sermon. Delivered in

short barking sentences slightly reminiscent of the parade ground, his material invariably links a thoughtful spiritual theme with issues of the day and sends the congregation home with much on which to reflect. He believes in challenging his hearers to some kind of response and frequently is heard to say that a sermon which does not call for action is not worth preaching. He is frequently asked to occupy the pulpit in churches outside his own archdeaconry and is sometimes invited outside the diocese.

He has one unusual habit that divides opinion among the clergy. From time to time, he might drop in on a Sunday unannounced and sit at the back of the church during the main service, and then arrange to visit later in the week for what he describes as "a conversation". Often these visits are commendatory—"Good and interesting sermon which must have helped a number of folk. You've got a good cross-section in your congregation, but I'd suppress the lady who led the prayers. Poison!" Occasionally, there is the reverse. "From the back I couldn't hear you—you have a tendency to mumble. Don't feel I missed much though. Elderly congregation and even then a bit thin on the ground." Sometimes he does the same at meetings of a Parochial Church Council. In this case, he has no legal right to be present, but no one on the council, including the vicar, ever has the courage to tell him so. A few days later comes "the visit", usually with helpful comments on the vicar's skills as chairman or suggestions how some of the business discussed could lead to useful developments in the parish.

The archdeacon almost certainly knows the nickname given him by the clergy—Fussy Fred. Invented by some wag a few years ago, it has stuck because everyone knows that he is utterly demanding in everything and in the parishes wants every "i" dotted and every "t" crossed. This relates especially to his view of worship. Fussy Fred never tires of reminding his clergy that the Church of England should be proud that wherever in England you might attend worship, you can expect a service taken from one of the Church's Prayer Books, old or new. He is fond of telling guilty priests: "If you start meddling with services and putting bits in here and there which you think are an improvement, you are simply being arrogant and unhelpful. Keep to the Prayer Books." The archdeacon himself always uses the centuries old Book of Common Prayer with no frills. He inspects parish Baptism, Marriage and Funeral Registers with great care to make sure they are accurately and carefully completed, as he does with the many other papers, documents and returns a parish priest has constantly to complete. His inspection of church buildings and halls is notorious; no broken drain, loose slate or shabby room escapes his attention. It is common knowledge among his colleagues that if he is involved in making any appointment to a post, all references and paperwork will be read carefully before the interview at which he will be the one who asks the most probing questions.

The most significant recurring event in the archdeacon's diary is the monthly staff meeting, chaired by the diocesan bishop and attended by his suffragan bishop, the cathedral dean, his brother archdeacon and the diocesan secretary. Sometimes a proposed change might be suggested in the life of the diocese and more often than not the archdeacon will be against it. "The old ways are best" is his usual response to most proposals for reform from parish boundary changes to new mission ideas or worship initiatives. There is frequently underlying tension in the meeting between Roberts and Archdeacon Smith, who looks after the northern part of the diocese, and who is "High Church" and fond of colourful and ritualistic worship. Roberts thinks he is disorganized and inclined to be lazy and is not above snide comments to this effect. The bishop is a mild man and a gentle chairman of the meeting, and is sometimes hurt by Roberts' blunt tone and lack of delicacy: "This priest is bone idle and a waste of space. We need to move him on. He needs a bit of hassle. Leave it to me. I'm good at that." The bishop blinks at such outbursts and gently moves the meeting forward.

The archdeacon is much respected by his brother clergy in spite of his straightforward and unvarnished approach to life, but from time to time he gets matters badly wrong. One of his larger parishes has a long tradition of High Church worship; it is claimed that famous names like Keble, Pusey and Newman preached there in Victorian times. The vicar is a single, rather artistic priest who the archdeacon has long suspected of being gay, a way of life about which he had secret reservations. One day he is told that inscribed in rough painted lettering on the wall of a male lavatory in the marketplace of this parish is a claim that the vicar did unmentionable things with choirboys. Roberts is incensed and jumping to the conclusion this could well be true of this particular priest telephones the man immediately. "Come and see me at the archdeaconry tomorrow morning" he instructed the surprised priest. On being asked by the man the reason for this sudden request, he is amazed to be told: "Oh dear, Archdeacon. Do you always believe things you see scrawled on walls? I have no intention of coming to see you." Later that night in bed he talks the matter over with his wife Louise who says: "Oh dear. You were rather rash. Things must be reversed. You should go and see this poor man and apologize." Her quiet wisdom regularly keeps him from making serious mistakes.

Archdeacon Roberts is of course ambitious. He would rather like to wear the purple and be No. 1 in the diocese instead of being lower down the pecking order. The general view in Lichfield is that this is unlikely. He is too outspoken, too lacking in tact and wisdom, and too much of a "character". Such an appointment might be risky and not in keeping with the steady, traditional stable from which bishops are usually drawn.

# 6

# The Man of the World

## The Reverend Mark Robarts

If any man was born with a silver spoon in his mouth, it is Mark Robarts, Vicar of Framley. Elder son of a prosperous doctor in Exeter, he is sent to the same private tutor as a young peer of the realm, and the two soon become close friends. They go on together to Harrow and then to Oxford, where Robarts mixes in "the best sets" before becoming a priest at 25. He serves just one year as a curate, before his friend's mother appoints him vicar of the rich family living of Framley, a piece of good fortune which would have been coveted by many priests 20 years older than he. The good Lady Lufton follows up this remarkable generosity by putting in his way an attractive and eligible young lady who quickly becomes Mrs Robarts, his loving wife and devoted mother of his children.

This fortunate young vicar likes to live well. In Victorian times, a horse took the place of a car, and "Mark, good priest though he was, was quite worldly enough to be fond of a good horse" and is always to be seen about on a smart sleek thoroughbred. In place of today's BMW convertible, he keeps a good stable, and when buying a horse, the "vicar did look at his bones, examining the brute in a very knowing and clerical manner", rather as now you would look at the engine and bodywork of a vehicle for sale.

But sadly, this manly, tall, fair-haired priest who dresses himself so "that no one should ever observe of him that his clothes were either good or bad, shabby or smart" has serious chinks in his armour. Above all, he delights in accepting invitations to country house weekends where he is able to rub shoulders with the great and the good. A social climber fond of horses, he has a natural fondness for fox hunting, a sport attracting many of the "county set" with whom Mark loves to spend time. This is particularly unfortunate, because a hunting parson was considered bad form in Victorian days and it brings down on him the ire of Lady Lufton, his neighbour and benefactor.

Our vicar is deeply aware that his recreational tastes invite problems. He constantly seeks to justify himself by recalling that the task of a priest is to mix with all levels of society, rich as well as poor. Yet beneath lies the constant lure of ambition. "Of whom generally did Prime Ministers and official bigwigs think it expedient to make bishops and deans? Was it not, as a rule, of those clergymen who had shown themselves able to perform their clerical duties efficiently and able also to take their place with ease in high society?" He knows the value of making friendships in high places and, on leaving for a country house visit, tells his wife: "Harold Smith . . . will be there . . . I cannot afford to neglect such a man's acquaintance." Harold Smith was likely to be in the Cabinet and might exercise considerable influence on senior clerical promotions.

Disaster lies ahead on all fronts. Our vicar learns there are rogues and swindlers at the top of the social tree as well as at the bottom. Nathaniel Sowerby, an MP and the owner of a country mansion much frequented by Robarts, turns out to be one of them. Knowing that the vicar is a man of means, Sowerby goes out of his way to flatter him and engineers an invitation for him to a weekend party at a duke's castle, something he knows Mark will find impossible to resist. During the weekend, Sowerby persuades the priest, against his better judgement, to sign a negotiable bill guaranteeing £400 in order to deliver Sowerby from current pressing financial embarrassments.

Mark Robarts will live to regret this signature forever. The complicated mechanism of Victorian bills is hard to follow but soon he is persuaded to sign a fresh bill for £500. Sowerby promises that this is simply another guarantee; it will not involve producing any ready cash and will bring all problems to an end. No great surprise, then, that after weeks of agonising pain and distress for the vicar and his family the only result is a final cash demand from moneylenders for £900. The good vicar has no more understanding of bills than we have today, constantly asserting that he never handled a penny of the money. By the time Sowerby attempts to get him to sign a third bill, he has learnt his lesson and flatly refuses.

The sorry story ends as Robarts faces the indignity of bailiffs arriving at the vicarage to compile an inventory of all his possessions prior to execution being levied to meet his debts. The distress caused to a much-respected vicar of a rural parish and to his wife and family can only be imagined, along with all the local publicity given to the event. News travels fast in the country. Happily, Lord Lufton, the vicar's neighbour and life-long friend, arrives in the nick of time as bailiffs come to take the inventory. He pays all money due on the spot, delivering the priest from further embarrassment.

Financial disaster is not the only trial the vicar faces. His clerical ambition takes a serious nosedive. His ill-fated friendship with Sowerby has led the great Harold Smith, now in the Cabinet, to arrange for Robarts to be offered the post of a prebendary at Barchester Cathedral. This is an appointment which would put his feet on the first rung of the clerical ladder, make him a dignitary of the Church and give him a stall in the cathedral, an additional £600 p.a. and a fine house in the Cathedral Close. As the appointment involves only occasional residence in Barchester during some months of the year, it could be held alongside his parish, and Robarts is delighted by the offer. He goes up to London the very next day to put the acceptance wheels in motion, telling his wife: "Prebendal stalls, Fanny, don't generally go begging long among parish clergymen. How could I reconcile it to the duty I owe to my children to refuse such an increase in my income?"

The delight does not last. He soon begins to feel that those dreadful bills leave no option but withdrawal of his acceptance of the glittering prebendal prize. He imagines his appointment might easily be seen as a reward for signing the bills and could look as if he has bribed his way into the post. He shares his intentions with Lord Lufton and Sowerby, but both reassure him that such a rash step is quite unnecessary and, glad to put such thoughts from his mind, he enters into the duties of a cathedral prebendary and the fruits of office. When news comes that bailiffs will arrive at the vicarage, however, Robarts knows that he cannot continue. All hope of continuing as a prebendary is lost, although his wife cannot understand why this should be; she tells him he has done nothing wrong and should continue in office. But her husband knows better. He replies with a sob: "How am I to go into the church and take my place before them all when everyone will know that the bailiffs are in the house?" We are told " . . . he wished with all his heart that he had never become a sharer in the good things of the Barchester Chapter." He duly resigns the cathedral appointment—just in time. A few days later *The Thunderer*—*The Times* of the day—runs an editorial advising him to take this step, and opining that "the evil which has now been done in Barchester is exactly the sort of mischief which follows the exaltation of unfit men to high positions". They are words that do not bring comfort to our hero.

Yet despite all these setbacks Robarts remains a good priest. In the midst of his problems, Lady Lufton persuades a neighbouring vicar to take him to task over his manner of life and the company he keeps, and when this interview takes place, Mark responds by breaking down in sobs, only too aware of his failures and weakness in resisting temptation. On an earlier occasion, this same brother priest, Josiah Crawley, was charged with theft and had to face the magistrates. The local gentry suggested Robarts as the best person to visit the accused and persuade him to engage a lawyer, and Dr Tempest, a senior Barchester vicar, approaches Robarts to advise Crawley saying: "I've an idea you could do more for this poor man than anyone else in the diocese." It transpires that Robarts had earlier generously stood bail for the man. When Tempest later approached Robarts to serve on a significant Commission, he describes him as "a man of the world and a clever fellow . . . not in awe of anybody".

Trollope neatly sums up the story of Mark Robarts when he writes: "He had been fond of pleasure and had given way to temptation,—as is so customarily done by young men of six-and-twenty, who are placed beyond control and have means at their command. Had he remained a curate until that age, subject in all his movements to the eye of a superior, he would, we may say, have put his name to no bills, have ridden after no hounds, have seen nothing of the iniquities of Gatherum Castle. There are men of twenty-six as fit to stand alone as they ever will be—fit to be prime ministers, heads of schools, judges on the bench—almost fit to be bishops; but Mark Robarts had not been one of them. He had many aptitudes for good, but not the strengthening courage of a man to act up to them. The stuff of which his manhood was to be formed had been slow in growth, as it is with many men . . . " This is a man who will live again and win.

## The Reverend Grant Willis

We have little control over our appearance and none at all over our parentage, but Grant Willis is fortunate on both counts. The phrase "tall, dark and handsome" could have been invented for him while his father, Stephen, was chairman of one of the UK's major banks, with an office in the City and an annual salary and bonus which would finance a small business. Grant was sent to the same prestigious school in Berkshire that Stephen had attended and then went on to an Oxford college with links to his school. His main interest at college was cricket; he captained the University First XI and alongside this managed a First-Class degree in Classics, something few serious sportsmen achieve.

At school, Grant had little interest in the Church. Like everyone else, he went to school chapel and enjoyed lustily singing hymns if they had a good tune, but apart from this religion meant nothing. Oxford brought about a change of seismic proportions. In his college, a man called Alistair lived in the college room below, a great supporter of the University Christian Union. With his friends Alistair was known to hold prayer meetings in his room for the souls of undergraduates living above him, and it was a college "in" joke that you could always tell these men by their hunted looks.

In the Easter term of Grant's last year, the Christian Union held a mission to the university. One evening, during a light-hearted conversation after dinner, Alistair bet Grant a bottle of champagne he wouldn't join him at one of the meetings. Grant was amazed to find Alistair was not teetotal, laughed and accepted the bet, saying that Alistair could look forward to enjoying a free bottle of the best when the mission was over. Reflecting on the deal, Grant wondered why he should give Alistair a bottle for not doing what he had no intention of doing anyway and decided it would be fun to go along to a mission meeting just for the sake of taking a bottle off Alistair afterwards. So, one night he did join him at the mission.

The rest, as they say, is history. What Grant heard that night made him reassess his attitude to Christian faith, and some weeks later he became a convinced Christian and regular worshipper in the College Chapel. His father intended his son should follow him into banking and had arranged that after university Grant should become an intern in the bank, but Grant convinced Stephen that before taking on the internship he would like to have a gap year. The expectation was that this year would be spent overseas, and his father was amazed to hear that Grant had decided instead to give the year to a body set up to promote Christian faith among university students. He started a job on a small salary which involved travelling around universities and colleges all over the UK encouraging and supporting student Christian Unions. At the close of the year, Stephen was even more amazed when his son had decided to abandon thoughts of banking and become a clergyman, telling him: "I'm not sure you know what you are doing. It's a great mistake to throw all your gifts and ability into the dustbin of the Church of England."

Undeterred, Grant entered a theological college in his beloved Oxford to train as a priest. The father of a fellow student was vicar of a well-known parish church in London's West End and was looking for a curate to follow one who was just leaving. Grant went down to London, was interviewed for the post and appointed; the vicar was delighted to have recruited such a promising colleague to serve his large congregation which attracted students and young people from all over London. Before long, Grant was delighted to discover his father had become reconciled to this change of life, and as Grant developed into a fine preacher, Stephen even occasionally came to hear him. He quickly became much loved by the congregation, organized a series of "away" weekends for younger members at a conference house in Surrey and cheerfully and effectively played his part in all aspects of parish life.

One day towards the end of his third year at the church, he was invited to a party at the flat of a friend from his Oxford days and met Angela, a contemporary who had read history at another college in Oxford. Grant had not known her then, but they had many common memories, were mutually attracted and "clicked". Angela was Grant's first serious girlfriend, and he was intoxicated by her. After a whirlwind courtship they got engaged, and he often got fun out of replying to the question "What does your fiancée do?" by responding that she was a call girl. In fact, she was a BT management trainee, based in an office in Croydon. Within months, the vicar officiated at their marriage in the church, and they set up home in the curate's flat in central London.

Stephen Willis belonged to a Pall Mall Club. One day over lunch at the Members' Table, he found himself sitting next to one of a number of bishops who were fellow members. He proudly told the bishop about his son, his recent marriage and the parish, and their talk led on to Grant's future. The bishop told Stephen that the vicar of an attractive small market town in mid-Sussex would soon be retiring. "He's been there over 30 years, and the place is decaying around him. I urgently need a strong able young priest to pull things together. Perhaps your son might be interested?" The bishop went on to talk of a lovely old rectory next to the church which the newlyweds might welcome. He mentioned that the appointment would normally go to an older, more experienced priest, but Grant's youth and his three years of experience in the go-ahead London parish would bring the injection of flair the parish so desperately needed.

As Grant was coming to the end of his three-year curacy, he jumped at this unexpected opportunity. The churchwardens of the parish were delighted when they met with him, and before many months had elapsed, Grant and Angela found themselves installed in the rectory of what proved to be an opulent parish with an ancient church, stuffed with prosperous London commuters along with a leaven of long-established locals. Angela joined the commuting brigade on the platform every morning.

Sadly, all this promise quickly faded. Angela's commuting left her very tired at the end of the week, and she rarely made a Sunday appearance in church, a habit which some of the congregation began to note and comment on. Grant began to realize that she did not seem to share his own deep commitment to faith, and as the months went past, they began to grow apart. Things were not helped when Angela made it clear that her top priority was her corporate career, and she was not sure about having a family. Before long, she accepted a post as manager of a BT local office in Gloucester and took a flat there during the week, only spending weekends in Sussex. Tongues began to wag further among the congregation, and Grant soon became aware he and Angela did not have a future together. Looking back, he realized they had married too swiftly, had been blinded by their first love and had not talked prudently through what the future involved. After weeks of difficult conversations, they parted and petitioned for divorce.

In the years that followed, Grant threw himself into his parish work, and between that and keeping the rectory afloat with the help of a cleaner and support from sympathetic parishioners, he had little time to think. Three years later, he felt it was time to move away from Sussex and make a fresh start elsewhere.

Such a move proved more difficult than he had imagined. He went to see his bishop who had appointed him and found him much less helpful than at first, saying that finding another parish in the diocese might not prove easy as "clergy these days were tending to stay longer in their parishes", although he did promise to add Grant's name to the transfer list. Grant decided to look further afield and responded to a number of parish posts advertised in the church press, but never seemed to get included in shortlists or asked for an interview. Reluctantly he was driven to the conclusion that although, like society, the church had publicly become more tolerant of divorce and there were a number of divorced clergy in prominent positions, there was still an in-built deep prejudice when it came to parish appointments. He was paying dearly for his youthful mistake with Angela. But this was a man who would live again and win. Today he is a bishop himself.

# 7

# The Snob

## The Very Reverend Henry Lovelace, Dean of Brotherton

A high point in the career of the Dean of Brotherton was the day when, visiting none other than the Marquis of Brotherton in his London hotel room, he violently pushed His Lordship into the fireplace after the Marquis used "an abominable word" to describe Mary, the dean's greatly loved daughter. Trollope's writing here is superb:

> . . . the lord had expected it so little . . . the dean had got him by his cravat and shirt-collar before he had begun to expect such usage as this . . . fire flashed from the clergyman's eyes, and his teeth were set fast, and his very nostrils were almost ablaze. . . . the dean, having got the victim's back to the fireplace, and having the poor wretch now fully at his command, threw the man with all his strength into the empty grate . . . the Marquis fell like a heap into the fender.

The Marquis had lived in Italy for many years, and news had reached England that he was now married and had a son. There was doubt about whether this infant child in Italy—who would be the heir if born in wedlock—had been so born. The dean's hotel meeting had been designed to establish the truth of this delicate matter and promised to be a difficult occasion. It ended more dramatically than even the dean had expected.

You may begin to wonder why the dean should be so interested in the child's pedigree. The short answer is he is an incorrigible social climber. The family seat of the Marquis, Manor Cross, is not far from the cathedral over which the dean presides, and he got enormous pleasure from visiting the Manor as frequently as possible and cultivating its aristocratic inhabitants. With the reigning Marquis absent in Italy, the family—his three sisters and elderly mother—is presided over by his younger only brother, Lord George. The dean has become intimate with them all, perhaps helped by the fact the family are of the High Church persuasion, while the bishop is decidedly Low Church and not welcome at Manor Cross. Conveniently, Lady Alice, one of the sisters, has also struck up a friendship with one of the cathedral canons, and this gives the dean even more excuse to frequent Manor Cross and enjoy its patrician delights, while fostering the relationship that leads to Lady Alice's marriage to the canon.

But there is more. The dean's only daughter Mary, a young, attractive and eligible lady, has inherited a considerable fortune from one of her grandparents, and is rich. Lord George, up at Manor Cross, is extremely poor. The family there decided the answer to his problem was on the very doorstep and their idea soon reached the dean. Not surprisingly, he was immediately attracted to the scheme, which would greatly extend his social ambitions. He himself arranged for Lord George to visit the deanery and propose marriage to Mary, who was rather overcome by events. Looking ahead, the dean is intoxicated by the immense social advantages. He will now become not just a visitor to Manor Cross but part of the family itself. Lord George is the presumptive heir to the title, and when the Marquis died, the dean will become father-in-law to a Marquis, and his own precious daughter a Marchioness. The glory of it! Then, if Mary has a son, his nephew would be Lord Popenjoy and heir to the title. Consumed with social ambition, the dean successfully encourages Mary to accept Lord George's overtures, despite the fact she has reservations about him and is not in love. The dean even writes the letter informing Mary's suitor of her acceptance, signing it himself.

It is easy to imagine the chagrin with which the dean greeted the news from Italy that the Marquis—a rude and unpleasant man—now has a son and heir, shattering all the decanal dreams. We are told he jumped from his chair when he heard the news. Happily, the circumstances surrounding the birth and the dates related to the marriage of the Marquis cast doubt on whether the heir was in fact entitled to be Lord Popenjoy. The dean is quite determined that he and Lord George together should leave no stone unturned to extract the truth from the Marquis, and it was this task which led to that memorable meeting in the London hotel room. Happily for the dean, it can be recorded that later in the story both the Marquis and his infant son died, the news being greeted with great triumph at the deanery. His Mary became a Marchioness and her infant son a future Marquis. All he had ever wished for came to pass.

Henry Lovelace's great concern with social status springs from his own lack of it. He had risen in the clerical ranks through hard work and a strong reputation as a preacher, but his stock was not that from which deans of the day were traditionally drawn. One side of his family had been stable keepers and the other side tallow chandlers, and this humble background was continually thrown in his face. When his aunt, Miss Tallowax, who we are told "was not brought up as a lady", lunched at Manor Cross and was shown around the house by the family she was ill at ease with such grandeur and the noble family in turn was unhappy with this connection with the dean. Lady Sarah, the eldest sister, thought he was "vulgar" and "not a man whom I like to trust altogether", while on another occasion she says: "I have always liked the dean personally . . . but he isn't . . . he isn't quite . . . ". "No, he isn't quite . . . " said Lord George, also hesitating to pronounce the word understood by both of them. The Marquis, when reminded of the dean's low birth, had snarled "in a stable", and even when the dean was amused, we are told he "laughed aloud, more like the son of a stable-keeper than a dean".

Lord George, finding himself in a partnership of discovery with the dean to establish the truth about the Italian infant, "was always conscious of the dean's low birth, the stable-keeper and the tallow-chandler". To the peer, "blood was always more important than wealth", and we are told that "he greatly disliked the idea of putting himself into the dean's hands; of becoming a creature of the dean's. He felt the dean to be stronger than himself, endowed with higher spirit and more confident hopes. But he also felt the dean was—the son of a stable-keeper."

The dean is fond of the good things of life. We are told he "lived as a dean ought to live", while the table at Manor Cross was rather plain alongside "the comparative luxury of the deanery". His late wife's fortune has made the dean a rich man, but he never lost an opportunity to attract more, as when he reminded Lord George that treating the elderly Miss Tallowax with kindness and warmth on her visit to Brotherton would be advisable in view of her £20,000.

It is not surprising that alongside the dean's material interests he enjoys a secular style of life. He smokes cigars and is much given to hunting, an activity at the time widely considered an inappropriate clerical activity. He enjoys a self-indulgent lifestyle, and we are told that "The dean up in London was to be a man of pleasure rather than a clergyman. He had no purpose either of preaching at St. Paul's or at the Abbey. He was going to attend no Additional Curates Society or the Sons of the Clergy", and instead of these things makes the most of the dinners and parties of the London season, in between riding in the best of company in Rotten Row. He is given to expressing himself in secular language when roused, making his daughter "startled by such a word from her father's mouth", and on another occasion telling Mary that if she is annoyed by the conversation of a troublesome person, she has only to "put her down"; not quite the clerical pastoral touch. He describes the Marquis as "a degraded animal", who is his enemy for ever after the insult to his daughter. "There could be no forgiveness. He could not find room in his heart for even a spark of pity because the man had lost an only child."

There is no denying that the dean is a powerful figure; Lord George has discovered that behind the low birth are great qualities of determination and vigour. Here is a character who could be cordial and warm, sagacious in his dealings, who speaks Italian, who is "urbanity itself" and "certainly the most popular man in Brotherton". There is also little doubt he is held in high esteem by his own cathedral staff, so that when he tells them the Marquis fully deserved the treatment received in that hotel room, they replied sincerely, "That is what we think." It is also well known that the bishop had no power in the Cathedral Close, so that the dean, when telling the hotel story to the bishop, said: "I tell it to you, not because you are bishop of the diocese, and I the dean of this cathedral—and as such, I am in such a matter by no means subject to your lordship's authority—but because of all my neighbours you are the most respected."

We are told little of Dean Lovelace's clerical work, apart from the fact that he has not made himself dear to the Bench of Bishops generally and that he has written a book "which had been characterised as tending to infidelity, and had more than once been invited to state dogmatically what was his own belief. He had never quite done so . . . " We can safely assume that he is not greatly given to pastoral work either and has never been a dedicated parish priest.

Much of the above is critical so it is fitting our picture of the dean should end on a positive note. His most memorable quality is an unchanging devotion and love for Mary. He not only arranges her marriage as the very best he felt she could make, but gives her support in every crisis she faces over the coming years. When she moved from the deanery to live with her husband at Manor Cross, he tutored her constantly in how to avoid being dominated by the family of the Marquis and went on to ensure her independence of them by acquiring a London home for her and Lord George, complete with a carriage, a necessary accessory in London social life. When there was a crisis in her marriage, it was to her father she turned, and when she left home on one occasion, it is recorded that he wept on being deprived of her company. Whatever the Dean of Brotherton's record as a priest, no man could have been a more devoted father to his only child.

## The Very Reverend Hugo Whitfield

Dean Whitfield lies sprawled in a comfortable deckchair in the rose garden of his sixteenth-century stone cottage in a Somerset village. Retirement is good. He would have preferred to have retired to his native Sussex or the Cotswolds, but prices there were out of reach. His mind runs lazily over the years. Why had he never married? The answer seemed simple. The few women with whom he had fallen in love were totally unsuitable as clergy wives, while the one woman he recalled who would have made a good wife for a priest lacked any polish or taste.

After serving for many years in parish ministry in London and in Surrey, he had unexpectedly been offered the post of Dean of Barfield in the north of England. Perhaps he had been mesmerized by those little words "dean" and "cathedral", but looking back, the whole thing had been a mistake. He recalled Tubby Fortescue, an old school friend. Tubby had ended up as owner of a string of restaurants in the North. He lived in a smart area of London and had a house in Barfield in which he stayed from time to time when looking after his business. He recalled Tubby coming to lunch one day at the deanery and over a brandy afterwards saying "Hugo, you have to face the fact there are few proper people living round here. There are the Trumpingtons out at Sandgrove Hall and the Marshalls out at Whitborough Manor, but beyond them, you have to agree, there aren't many civilized beings in these parts."

Tubby had been right. Hugo's years at Barfield had been a mistake and less than congenial. He recalled going out into the streets of the city and feeling he was surrounded by strange hordes who did not speak his language, flying back to the comfort of the deanery for shelter. It was just not his milieu. As the delightful scent of the roses wafts his way, he remembers some of the Barfield characters who had made his life a misery. There was Big Bessy, the large lady who headed up the Cathedral Flower Guild. She had seemed to be waiting round every corner, haranguing him in a voice that would have woken the dead, usually complaining about the kitchen facilities available to what she called "My Wonderful Team". Sam Marshall was another unhappy memory. A big accountant in the city, he had chaired an important cathedral committee with which Hugo had to have many dealings. Over lunch, Sam appeared to eat his food half in his mouth and half out; he often spat when he talked and his broad local accent was hard to follow. The words ambience, beauty and style were a foreign language to dear Sam. Even the organist, young Fred James, was rough at the edges. He produced music lacking in any feeling; his choir certainly sang with spirit and energy, but when you had said that you had said it all.

Four years in Barfield was enough. At 63, Hugo took early retirement and accepted an appointment as English Chaplain at Manton-sur-mere, a delightful coastal village on the French Riviera. There followed five of the happiest years of his life. The chaplaincy was based in an ancient house of good size not far from the beach. Every week a decent-sized congregation of English "expats" gathered in the attractive English Church for the Sunday morning service, which during the summer months was usually enlarged considerably by the addition of tourists from the UK. Happily, Hugo reflects as he reclines in the sun, tourists of the better class. His French was quite good, as he had always kept up the language, and his regular shopping sprees to nearby Nice gave him great pleasure. He would wander along the sea front or enjoy a quiet coffee outside a small café in a back street before driving along the coast road home.

Life at Manton was not too demanding. He much enjoyed taking a monthly house communion to old Sir James and Lady Willis out at their wonderful farmhouse a few miles inland. They were both housebound and unable to get to church but were still able to provide a decent lunch in their beautiful panelled dining room. There would be fascinating conversation about local personalities and politics, and together they would put the world to rights. In the winter months, there would be many invitations to drinks parties or lunches in the area, usually from UK visitors of the better sort wintering in the south of France. He recalls with pleasure hospitality dispensed by Lord and Lady Walsingham in their wonderful villa by the sea and the lunch parties in Nice at the English Club.

Hugo reflects that life in Somerset is suiting him well. As a retired dean, he has been "taken up" by the better class of family in the area and as a single man is a useful appendage at lunch or dinner parties in the county. He makes occasional forages to his Club in London to meet up with old friends, and has joined the Bath Club, based in a beautiful old Georgian house in the city, where he seems to be making new friends.

Yes, he does take occasional services in his village church when the vicar is away. But that is all. In Hugo's view, 40 years at the coalface is enough for any man.

# 8

# The Scholar

## The Very Reverend Francis Arabin, Dean of Barchester

Many an able university student has found that an addiction to parties, sport, travel or some other attraction has come at the cost of that expected First Class Honours degree. So it was with Francis Arabin. At school, he spent too much time writing poetry, failed to get a university entrance scholarship in Classics, and had to pay his own way at Oxford. At Balliol the habit continued, leading to a Second Class Honours degree, failure to obtain that coveted Balliol Fellowship, and life as an Oxford don seemingly beyond his grasp. Happily, the neighbouring Lazarus College obligingly took him in as a Fellow, and like all Fellows of his day he was ordained as a priest on appointment. Arabin went on to enjoy the congenial life of the comfortable Senior Common Room, engaging in spirited debate with his colleagues on the issues of the day. Soon he was appointed an Oxford Professor—of Poetry—and looked set to spend all his days in Oxford.

Down in Barchester in the West Country, Archdeacon Grantly had other ideas. Engaged in ongoing warfare with the new bishop and Obadiah Slope, his chaplain, Dr Grantly cast around for weapons in the battle. His fertile mind alighted on Arabin, a friend from Oxford days. Here was a keen mind and an expert debater, who would make a good front man in the struggle. There was a further great advantage. Arabin's poetic nature had led him to embrace the High Church party in the Church of England, drawn by rich vestments, elaborate ritual, sweet-savoured incense and a horror at the idea of women priests. A follower of the future Cardinal Newman, he had almost become a Roman Catholic, attracted by the idea of giving up all for his faith and embracing the spiritual disciplines of the Roman Church. He had only been dissuaded by the strong arguments of his college friend and fellow priest, Josiah Crawley. By contrast, Slope was an evangelical from the Low Church party, given to fervent, simple and unadorned worship. The two men would make strong protagonists.

Dr Grantly decided to offer Arabin the significant parish of St Ewold's, not far from Barchester, a good base from which to conduct hostilities. But why should a successful man forsake a comfortable Oxford berth for a West Country parish? Several helpful thoughts came to the archdeacon. Arabin had been in Oxford for some years, and a change of life could be attractive, while the Oxford man had already crossed theological swords with Slope in the national press. He might welcome the chance to continue the conflict at close quarters. The custom of the day would also enable Arabin to keep his rooms in Oxford and put in an experienced curate to run the parish, so that he would only need to make occasional forays down to St Ewold's. Dr Grantly was a good stage manager, travelling up to Oxford to make the offer in person, and making sure he did so in Lazarus College's impressive library with Dr Gwynn, the distinguished Master of the College, sitting alongside him. Who could resist?

Arabin is 40 years old when he arrives in Barchester as the new Vicar of St Ewold's. Above the middle height with jet black hair, he has a massive forehead and a gentleness around the mouth that speaks of a kind and generous nature. An academic to his fingertips, when talking on theological topics he can appear loquacious, arrogant and conceited, yet on all other topics is retiring and diffident. Oddly nervous and shy about his first appearance in a country parish, he tellingly remarked that a country priest might feel exactly the same if asked to preach in the University Church at Oxford. A man of perfect manners he loathes all unkindness or sarcasm; told he would soon be meeting Mr Slope for the first time at a party, he quietly responded he would do so "with pleasure". His humour takes the form of the droll wit of a scholar; any joke which produces actual laughter would not be his kind of joke. Here is a man of deep unseen emotions who needs to resort to poetry to express them.

In the event, the archdeacon's political astuteness is for nothing. Soon after arrival his champion's piercing logic and penetrating argument proves superfluous. The arrogant power-drunk bishop's chaplain falls out with his employer, is ignominiously dismissed and leaves the diocese in disgrace. Meanwhile, the new Vicar of St Ewold's, spending his first month living as a guest at the archdeacon's Plumstead Rectory, is left to discover new truths about himself.

Arabin soon realizes that an ascetic, celibate life devoted to worship and scholarship in the manner of a Roman priest has strong drawbacks. Enjoying Plumstead he becomes aware for the first time of the lure of an attractive house and garden, a well-stocked table and all the material delights money can bring. A little flame of jealousy arises as he notes the joys afforded by a loving wife, children and the warmth of family life. Watching the archdeacon surround himself with the best of everything, this quiet scholarly man feels he is missing out. He also notes the respect and honour in which the archdeacon is held as he moves around the diocese and sees something of the satisfaction that power and position can bring to a man. He groans inwardly; it is now too late to change course. He might shine outwardly, but his inner self realizes how much of life has passed him by. At 40, he is simply a country priest with a taste for greater things which will now never come his way.

Neither has life in an all-male Oxford college equipped Francis Arabin to understand women. He enjoys the company of pretty and amusing ladies, but to him they are children without feeling or understanding, not worth the effort of stretching himself in conversation. Barchester is to alter his thinking rather quickly on two fronts. Signora Neroni, a stunningly beautiful but disabled lady, daughter of a senior cathedral clergyman, is one of the feminine attractions of Barchester. She holds court in her home to many admirers, lying languidly on a couch in her drawing room, and one of those regularly gathered around is Arabin. He experiences an awakening. He sits bewitched, subjected to temporary delirium as the Signora's beautiful lips utter sweet nothings to him. This new experience is totally intoxicating, and he is drawn again and again to the Signora's parties, "he knew not why". At the same time—perhaps as a result of this new awakening to feminine charms—he feels himself secretly attracted to Eleanor, the archdeacon's attractive widowed sister-in-law. He has watched her moving around Plumstead Rectory, and they have enjoyed many conversations. Without really realizing it, he has fallen in love. Admiration, respect and even love has also been gradually creeping up on Eleanor's side as well, as she suddenly finds herself unaccountably jealous for the time Arabin spends with Neroni.

The Signora finds enormous pleasure in using her beauty and charm to captivate men in an utterly selfish way. She has probably never done an unselfish action in her life but, strange to record, she now embarks on one. Having extracted a confession of love for Eleanor from Arabin, she summons the surprised lady for a totally unexpected private audience at her couch. There Neroni tells a bemused Eleanor of his love, alerts her to expect an imminent proposal and warns that if his reserved and proud nature meets with a refusal, he will never again return. This remarkable interview lays the foundation for a happy and joyful marriage and must have left Neroni greatly pleased with herself.

As a scholar, Arabin now starts to analyse his feelings. Eleanor is a rich lady; might he be in love with money and not with her? Perhaps she has another admirer, and his love is doomed? Perhaps she doesn't care a straw for him, and the whole idea is pointless and should be abandoned? But such is the way of true love he presses on, and when the happy moment arrives, the two come together almost by osmosis. Few words are spoken. Arabin silently takes her hand in his, and she does not withdraw it. He knows. The moment "was sufficient to make it ever memorable for them both". He breathes her name, clasps her to him and never looks back, a spontaneous meeting of hearts and minds. The archdeacon had not invited his Oxford friend to stay at his house to find a wife but is quite delighted at the news. At that moment, a tear might have been observed in each of his eyes, a rare event indeed.

A wife is not the only good thing which comes from the archdeacon's champion moving to Barchester. The post of Dean of Barchester has lately fallen vacant and wheels begin to turn as the archdeacon and the Master of Lazarus again join forces. Pressure is put on the Bishop of Belgravia, who speaks confidentially to a Marquis high in the counsels of the realm. The Marquis plants a discreet word in the ear of the prime minister over a cup of coffee at Windsor Castle, after which "a distinguished person" blesses the scheme. Arabin emerges as the new dean.

The dean governs his cathedral with grace and wisdom, but his character remains unchanged. Ever grateful to Josiah Crawley for his earlier advice and counsel which had kept him in the Church of England, Arabin gives him a parish in the Barchester diocese, sending him gifts of money from time to time to alleviate his poverty. The dean continues to be devoted to the formality and colour of High Church worship and Eleanor comes to share his enthusiasm. She moves two degrees "up the candle" in her own worship as the happy couple come even closer together.

### The Very Reverend Dr Matthew Gibbs

Matthew Gibbs spent his childhood at Southcote Hall in Lancashire. Many local people were employed on the Southcote Estate, built up during Victorian times by the Gibbs family who had owned several cotton mills in the county. His father Richard was deeply involved in many aspects of the local community and also served as churchwarden at Southcote Parish Church, around which many of Matthew's early memories were centred. As a small boy, he had held the incense boat for the vicar, and at home during school holidays he was often pressed into service to act as a server at the Sunday morning service, when he would need to wear the appropriate garb. Southcote had a tradition of High Church worship, and from childhood Matthew knew all about church vestments, the appropriate colours for the different feasts of the Church and the number of candles there should be on the altar. Arriving as a schoolboy at Harrow, he had found worship in the school chapel rather Low Church compared with his home, although he was prepared for confirmation there by one of the school's chaplains. It was an experience he took very seriously and it meant a great deal to him.

During school holidays, Matthew had often amused himself on the hall's croquet lawn, and at Harrow he came to realize the rather amateur "knockabout" kind of croquet he played at home—culminating in sending his opponent's ball into the bushes—was only a substitute for the real game. He began to spend more and more time on the croquet lawn, perfecting his mastery of the yellow, red, blue and black balls and learning that proper croquet had more in common with chess than with physical skills. He even became a member of the Croquet Association, the sport's professional body. His schoolmasters did not approve of what soon became an addiction affecting his academic work; he was more than lucky to scrape a place at Oxford's St Edmund Hall to study Classics.

At Oxford, the "croquet bug" took an even more serious hold. In his final year, he was in the English Croquet Team that played in the World Croquet Championships in California and earned a "Blue" playing for Oxford against Cambridge. Slipping in alongside his croquet, Matthew had also developed an interest in public speaking, joining the Oxford Union and regularly taking part in their debates, and he became an accomplished speaker. It was at the Union that he got to know many of those of his contemporaries who would later become well known in politics and public life.

A gifted student, he was expected to be placed in the First Class in the Classical Moderations Examination in his second year but only managed an Upper Second. His tutors hoped he would repair this disappointment in his Final "Greats" Examination at the end of his fourth year. Sadly, there was a repeat performance, entirely due to croquet and debating, along with too much time spent in the college chapel, where he had become chapel steward, assisting the chaplain with service arrangements.

Matthew had hoped for a career in university teaching, but his second-class degree meant that neither St Edmunds nor any other Oxford college was able to offer him the fellowship for which he had longed. He pleaded with his tutor to be allowed to stay on at St

Edmund's to study for a doctorate and happily his Upper Second Class proved sufficient. He chose as his research project the Emperor Constantine and spent the next three years delving into dusty papers and manuscripts. Three years later, he was awarded his doctorate, which achieved considerable publicity in learned circles when it was published in book form with a lurid cover, under the title *Christ, Constantine and the Creeds*.

During those three years of research, Matthew found himself hard pressed financially and managed to persuade an Oxford church college that trained men and women to become priests to take him on for a few hours each week teaching Greek to some of the students. The few pounds this brought in was a great help; he enjoyed mixing with the student body and occasionally ate with them in the college. The experience resulted in something more than this small cash benefit; it changed his life. Always deeply involved in the Church of England, he developed deep respect and admiration for many of these potential priests, and after much thought, decided he too would abandon all ideas of an academic life and instead become a priest himself. After successfully going through a number of selection "hoops", he found himself in the study of the Bishop of Oxford discussing his future, which he hoped would mean quietly continuing in Oxford while training at the college which had inspired him. It was not to be. The bishop was firm: "You have been now seven years in Oxford, and you need to get out. I'm sending you to a church college in Yorkshire run by monks. The worship there should suit you and the training you will get will be rigorous. After that a spell in the East End of London as a curate would do you no harm."

For good or ill, things did not work out this way. Towards the end of his time in Yorkshire and just before he was due to be ordained, the dean of his old college suggested that instead of going to a normal curacy in a parish, he might consider becoming the junior college chaplain at St Edmund's, assisting the dean with his care of the students and continuing his training under the dean's direction. Happily, the bishop was miraculously persuaded that Matthew's talents would be wasted in the East End, realizing that a college chaplaincy could be the better option. There followed four happy years as a chaplain at St Edmund's, and because of the considerable success of his book, the Director of Studies in Classics agreed that he could also teach Classical History to several small tutorial groups of undergraduates. He quickly became popular with both the fellows of the College and the student body, and when, towards the end of his time as chaplain, the dean of the college announced his retirement, Matthew was appointed his successor. He now became a full Fellow of the college, popular in the Senior Common Room and at high table, and with a job for life.

These years proved to be eventful. Matthew built on the reputation resulting from his book on Constantine and published many articles in theological journals, mainly

on church history. Alongside this, he established a wide
reputation as a preacher and lecturer with a constant
stream of contributions on church issues in national
newspapers and journals and occasional appearances
on radio and television. Still not yet 40, he was settling
into a secure and wholly pleasant Oxford life, although
accompanied by occasional pangs of conscience that
his world was just a little too comfortable. Towards the
end of one summer, he was invited to lunch by Henry
Wilson, an old friend from student days, a priest who
had recently become an archdeacon in the southwest.
They met at the archdeacon's London Club in Pall Mall,
and over lunch Henry set out his stall. A major, town-
centre parish in the diocese needed a new vicar. It had
a large, spectacular Norman church, always served by a
priest of outstanding talent and ability who had usually
gone on to greater things. More particularly, the diocese
was woefully short of able priests from the Catholic
High end of the Church, and there was a danger that
the evangelical party was in the ascendant; the balance
needed to be kept. Would Matthew consider leaving
Oxford and coming to the archdeacon's rescue over
this crucial appointment? Returning home, Matthew
said his prayers and reflected that his Oxford life was
perhaps a shade too easy and that a new and challenging
direction might be no bad thing. After ten days of deep
thought, he decided on a total change in his life's course,
and three months later left Oxford for a new life as Vicar
of Shireshead, 40 miles from Bristol.

It is very much a new life after the cloistered academic calm of Oxford. Matthew is deeply grateful that he has inherited an able curate from his predecessor, who has now become a bishop in the north of England. Matthew has been a clergyman for 14 years and has never worked in a parish before. To begin with he leans heavily on his curate's experience, although he is a quick learner and has a natural rapport with people of all backgrounds. Soon he begins to find his feet and enjoys the deeply varied life of a parish priest. Home is a fine Georgian rectory near the church with a large airy study and a private chapel opening off it. Over the study mantelpiece is a stone sculpture of the arms of St John the Baptist, the dedication of the church, with inscribed beneath "A voice crying in the wilderness". They are words he sometimes thinks particularly apt as he prepares his sermons.

Matthew has never regretted his move to Shireshead. Often, coming out of the house, he meets a lady who lives in one of the flats in a tall Victorian building directly opposite the rectory, and they have struck up a friendship. Charlotte Young is a journalist on *The Times*, with many interests, and he greatly enjoys their occasional conversations. Matthew has little experience of women; at school there had only been boys, while at St Edmund's there had been just a sprinkling of girls, as the college had only begun to admit them a few years before his arrival. He has always enjoyed female company but has never taken it seriously; women cannot be expected to say or do anything significant in Matthew's view, although they can be quite entertaining. He is firmly against women priests. With Charlotte, Matthew has a rude awakening—she is both attractive and highly intelligent with a quirky sense of humour, and their talks in the road soon develop into dropping into each other's houses for a drink or coffee and a good gossip. He isn't quite sure how it happened, but he seems to have fallen in love and begins to count the time to when he will see her again. After six months, matters reach a not unexpected conclusion; Matthew and Charlotte are married by the bishop in his own parish church, the background scenery to so many of their meetings. Over the years, Matthew has managed to keep up with his croquet; their wedding reception was—of course—held at the Shireshead Croquet Club.

Four years later, the Dean of Bristol died in office, and Matthew is enormously surprised to be offered this senior appointment at such an early age. He and Charlotte move into the comfortable deanery in the heart of a city of which he has always been fond. The decision to move on from Oxford has been the right one, although he never forgets the immense debt he owes his friend the archdeacon for that memorable London lunch.

# 9

# The Time Server

## The Reverend Mr Groschut, Bishop's Chaplain

Mr Groschut's name is a curious one, explained by the fact he is a converted Jew. He had become a Church of England priest of the Low Church evangelical variety, rising in later life to become chaplain to the Bishop of Brotherton. He is one of the few priests in Trollope not to be given a Christian name, possibly an expression of a little antipathy on the part of his clerical creator. A person of some distinction, he is an able theological scholar, an honorary canon of the cathedral and a member of its governing body, the chapter.

Mr Groschut's first priority in all things is total loyalty to the bishop, a quite proper quality. Yet, like many bishops' chaplains down the ages, he frequently uses his position as an excuse to further his own ends. He is an expert in the words parroted by chaplains in every diocese: "The Bishop was inclined to think that this or that might be done", or "This is the Bishop's view of the matter."

His relationship with Henry Lovelace, Dean of Brotherton, has never been ideal. It is well known throughout Brotherton that the dean never allows the bishop to interfere in the affairs of the cathedral. Lovelace frequently has to make it clear that this rule also applies to the bishop's chaplain. In return, Mr Groschut allows his loyalty to the bishop to translate into extreme antipathy towards the dean, never letting an opportunity pass when he might lower the dean in the eyes of the bishop by carrying gossip back to him from the cathedral. The dean has come to view the chaplain as a thorn in his side.

The dean is something of a character around Brotherton and its cathedral, so the chaplain is not short of stories to carry back to the bishop's palace. One of his favourite themes is the dean's addiction to fox hunting; he is frequently to be seen riding to hounds with the local hunt. As we have seen, in late Victorian times, this particular pastime was not viewed as appropriate for a clergyman and few priests risked the opprobrium involved. So it is a rich theme for the chaplain to exploit. Sadly, he is always disappointed with his episcopal lord and master's response, who never treats such news with the degree of seriousness he feels it deserves, even after Groschut has assured him "a bishop is as much entitled to cause enquiry to be made into the moral conduct of a dean as of any other country clergyman in his diocese". Mr Groschut is a man of many parts and a Brotherton character, the owner of a local newspaper entitled

*The Brotherton Church.* As the bishop fails to take a sufficiently serious view of the dean's sporting habits, the chaplain arranges for the matter to be adversely raised in the columns of his paper, causing the dean to be drawn into a public controversy he later regrets.

The chaplain feels that the bishop's failure to respond to gossip about the dean is especially strange when this gossip appears to him to be especially damaging. He never stops telling his master that on one occasion the dean had pitched the local Marquis into the fireplace of his London hotel room. Surely such behaviour cannot be allowed to go unpunished? He is horrified to get the simple and rather dry episcopal observation that the dean no doubt had good reason for his action. This then causes the chaplain to comment that such violence could cause the police to be involved. The bishop quietly replies: "I know nothing about the police." On returning home, the chaplain tells his mother the bishop is getting old, and a firmer and younger man now needs to take over the diocese.

Even on social occasions, the chaplain never loses the opportunity to annoy his protagonist. In normal circumstances, he would never be invited to dine at the deanery, but on one occasion he deputizes for the bishop. In conversation over dinner, he takes the opportunity to deliver several sallies in "clerical pugnacity", and eventually suggests that "the hilarity of the diocese might be enhanced by certain evangelical festivities", and that such occasions might be held in the Cathedral

Close. The dean, unruffled, responds that meetings in the Close were normally held in the deanery and then adds drily: "Of all meetings I like such as this the best. Pass the bottle."

The knowledge that the dean's daughter Mary is particularly close to him opens up another possible line of attack, and the chaplain becomes active in spreading unpleasant rumours about her. Mary is married to Lord George, a local aristocrat, and on one occasion, her husband went back to his old home to visit his family, while Mary stayed at the deanery to be with her father. Mr Groschut did not scruple to spread the story that the marriage was in trouble because of Mary's unwise London friendship with a fancy-free bachelor and that her husband's family would not even receive her, so that Lord George was forced to visit his family alone. To this was added further gossip about her busy social life in London and love of dancing. It is no surprise that Mary describes the chaplain as "my pet abomination", going on to say: "I think I really do hate Mr. G. I almost do wish they would make him a bishop of some unhealthy place ... and that once there the mosquitos could eat him day and night."

Mary almost gets her wish. The chaplain has created problems for himself by becoming engaged to the daughter of a Brotherton bookseller but has later gone back on the arrangement. Her father has visited the bishop and Mr Groschut's employment at the bishop's palace has drawn to a close more rapidly than he would have wished. The bishop has grown more than tired of his chaplain's endless gossip and is glad of this opportunity to offer him the parish of Pugsty, telling him: "It's Pugsty or nothing." Now Pugsty is a most undesirable place on the edge of the Potteries, giving both the dean and Mary considerable satisfaction.

## The Reverend Canon David Faulkner, Bishop's Chaplain

The Reverend Canon David Faulkner is just 60 and has been Vicar of Little Chester for 12 years. He was given the title of Honorary Canon of the cathedral some time ago, but if truth were told had hoped to become an archdeacon. It never happened. Now, over the washing up in the kitchen, David tells his wife Mary that he feels he has "lost steam". He tells her that he is greatly looking forward to retirement with no more difficult church council meetings, no strangers banging on the vicarage door, no late-night emergency pastoral visits to the local hospital.

In another kitchen, at the bishop's palace, the Right Reverend James Hopkins reminds us that even those who wear purple help with the washing up, if only occasionally. Andrew, his young chaplain, is coming to the end of his contract, and Hopkins tells his wife Charlotte that next time round he is thinking of an older man: "These young chaplains are all very well, but they seem to spend a lot of time at dinners and drinks parties ingratiating themselves with the great and the good. They don't always have an eye on managing things here." Charlotte agrees and adds that Andrew sometimes adopts a superior attitude to clergy twice his age: "I overheard him in the downstairs hall only this morning being patronizing to the Vicar of St Mary's and telling him the bishop thought something or other." "Yes", muses the bishop, "an older man could be more reliable and more efficient, and the senior clergy might feel happier dealing with him. I'll give it a try. David Faulkner over at Little Chester could do with a change in his last few years. I'll get him to pop over for a chat."

A few months later, David and Mary leave parish life and are installed in a spacious flat in the bishop's palace. David runs the office and is the bishop's gatekeeper, answers his emails, letters and telephone calls and accompanies him to most engagements in the diocese, usually driving the car. The bishop's palace is quite close to the cathedral, and the dean has a good and warm relationship with the bishop. David often sees the two men discussing church affairs or simply gossiping.

Sadly, David does not have a good relationship with Anthony, the dean, who a few years earlier had written an article in *Theology Today* expressing sympathy for gay priests and mildly advocating same-sex partnerships and same-sex marriage. David, always conservative on such matters, had penned a riposte to the dean, and a lengthy correspondence had taken place in the columns of the journal. There is also another disagreement; normally, as an honorary canon of the cathedral, David expects to be asked to preach there from time to time, but the dean rarely invites him. Nor is their relationship improved by the fact that the dean refuses to host an annual evangelical event in the cathedral which, before he arrived, had always taken place. He has even been heard to refer to it as "an evangelical jamboree", which offends David, who had been a regular attendee at the event. When the two men do meet around the Cathedral Close, there is a certain frostiness in the air. David remains resentful. He may never have become an archdeacon, but as bishop's chaplain he will teach the great dean a few lessons.

His first opportunity arises when a member of the cathedral chapter tells him that the dean has deliberately arranged the date of a visit to the cathedral by a royal duke on a day when he knew that the bishop would be at a residential conference abroad. Armed with what he thinks is a useful piece of dynamite, he tells the bishop one day over coffee. He replies airily: "Oh, I don't think Anthony would do such a thing; it's not his style. Anyway, even if I was here I probably wouldn't have gone—Anthony runs the cathedral, and it's right he should do the honours on the day." David is somewhat deflated. He feels the bishop is wrong to take matters quite so calmly.

Around this time, there is a problem in one of the parishes. The priest had taken over a thriving church with a large congregation, but it has been an unfortunate and sorry appointment, and within a few years the congregation has been decimated and reduced to a handful. The bishop has no specific grounds on which to dismiss the priest, and David knows that there has been endless discussion between the bishop, the dean, the archdeacon and other senior staff about how the matter should be resolved. Indeed, he has been present on several such occasions. He now hears from a number of sources that many people in the parish involved think that the bishop is "pussyfooting" around the matter. The dean has been heard to strongly agree with this view, and David takes an early opportunity to feed this piece of information to his master. Again, the bullet fails to reach its target. The bishop merely responds: "We all know this is a difficult situation, and there are many views floating about. I'd be surprised if the dean said anything of the kind. Whatever he may feel, he is by nature a discreet person."

There follows the famous occasion when a secretary in the cathedral office tells David that the dean often puts his arm around young ladies in the office, and there is constant talk about his conduct and whether it amounts to improper behaviour. David doesn't let the grass grow under his feet here. Reporting this conversation to the bishop, however, he is told: "The dean is a big tall man and a tactile kind of person, and goes round hugging everyone. He often puts his arm around Charlotte, and she thinks nothing of it." A few years later, with strict safeguarding precautions in place, things might have worked out in a different way.

By now, the bishop is becoming a little tired of David's constant murmuring about the cathedral and its dean. The matter is becoming a bore. After the chaplain has been with him just over three years, the bishop happens to be in the office one night looking for some paper clips. Not knowing where they are kept, he opens a drawer to discover a large pile of unopened letters from over a month ago. Clearly David has stuffed them in the drawer and forgotten to deal with them. Next day the chaplain suddenly finds his retirement nearer than he imagined, and three months later leaves the palace under a cloud and with a small financial settlement. Over a drink that evening, the bishop says to Charlotte: "Not much to choose between young and old it seems. There's always a problem with chaplains somewhere. Let's hope this new young man works out well."

# The "Psalms and Spiritual Songs" Priest

## The Reverend Mr Stumfold

Miss Mackenzie, a London based thirty-"something" spinster, inherits a comfortable legacy. She uses it to move out of London and starts a new life in Littlebath, Trollope's Bath, renting a comfortable apartment in the fashionable Paragon, a grand building bordered by high railings looking out onto Montpellier Gardens. She is soon visited by Mr Stumfold, a leading light of the Littlebath clerical scene, who loses no time in recruiting her to his congregation. Here is a priest who holds no attraction for Trollope, one of the few clergy in his priestly gallery who is given no Christian name.

Mr Stumfold has the charm and manners of a gentleman, well suited to ministering to the residents of the Paragon, a jovial man of indomitable energy, a welcome guest at any dinner party. Above all else he is an evangelical clergyman from the Low Church part of the Church of England, where worship is simple and uncluttered by candles, ritual or any formality. Miss

Mackenzie is as yet unaware of what being an evangelical entails, but she is soon to find out because Mrs Stumfold—no doubt at the bidding of her earthly lord and master—loses no time in inviting the newcomer to one of her famous vicarage tea parties. These gatherings are not simply social occasions but a basic weapon in Mr Stumfold's armoury as a priest, where evangelical truth is revealed. As his helpmeet explains, "Society with me, Miss Mackenzie, is never looked upon as an end in itself. It is only a means to an end. No woman regards society more favourably than I do. I think it offers to us one of the most efficacious means of spreading true gospel teaching . . . and Mr. Stumfold is of the same opinion."

These vicarage tea parties reveal to Miss Mackenzie that Mr Stumfold has decidedly strict views on morality and Christian behaviour. Card games of all types are anathema, dancing is of the devil, while horse riding and hunting are quite beyond the pale. Sunday is always called the Sabbath, and strict Sunday observance is always kept by the good evangelical, who attends at least two services every Sunday. The Post Office has been instructed not to deliver Sunday mail to members of Mr Stumfold's congregation in order that the sanctity of this holy day is not impaired. Miss Mackenzie had at first been attracted to the delights of Littlebath Assembly Rooms, where there was gaiety, cards and dancing but soon discovered that the Assembly Rooms and membership of the Stumfold tea party set cannot be mixed. It was either one or the other; a choice had to be made. In the Paragon, the social set, led by Mrs Todd, stands for worldly values and amusements, while another brigade follows the Stumfold way of life. Which set should Miss M. join? Carried along by indecision she eventually finds herself merging into the Stumfold tea party way of life. We hear that "she had thrown herself into the society of the saints, and now here could be no escape for her; she could not be wicked even if she wished it".

She discovers that Mr Stumfold "reigned over his own set as a tyrant, but to those who obeyed him he was never austere in his tyranny". Here is a priest who exercises strict discipline over his flock, ably assisted by his wife, making sure they do not fall into secular ways. This discipline even extends to personal matters. Miss Mackenzie will never forget receiving a stern visit from the priest's good lady who has suspected her of forming a romantic relationship with her husband's curate in the course of the tea parties in the vicarage drawing room. On that occasion, Miss Mackenzie properly tells the vicar's wife which direction to travel in, and the visit is not prolonged.

At the heart of the tea parties is holy scripture. On every occasion, there are Bible talks, and Miss Mackenzie learns that constant familiarity with the Good Book is the hallmark of being an evangelical. Indeed, she finds this familiarity excessive. When Mr Stumfold addresses these gatherings "she was astonished at the special freedom of his manner—how he spoke of St. Paul as Paul, declaring the saint to have been a good fellow; how he said he liked Luke better than Matthew, and how he named a holier name than these with infinite ease and an accustomed familiarity". She is shocked and notes that the ladies present skip to the tea table in the back drawing room with a light step "owing to the unceremonious treatment which St. Peter and St. Paul had received from their pastor". Another feature of the evangelical world which surprises her was the use of the Bible for conjuring up light-hearted puzzles. On one occasion, Mr Stumfold asks his tea party gathering: "Why was Peter in prison like a little boy with his shoes off?" When she gets home, Miss Mackenzie puzzles for an hour over that riddle, but gets no further. Pastor Stumfold also excels at using holy scripture to tickle and amuse his largely feminine tea party audience. It might be: "I'm not going to have anything more to say to Peter and Paul at present. You'd keep me here all night and the tea would be spoilt", or it could be, as he filled the glass of some old lady in his set "Wine maketh glad the heart of woman, Mrs Jones."

Another feature of the vicarage gatherings is the constant emphasis on human sin and failure. At one tea party, Mr Maguire, Mr Stumfold's curate, says to Miss Mackenzie: "When I look into my own heart, I see how black it is. It is full of iniquity; it is a sore that is ever running, and will not be purified", to which she replies "Gracious me, how unpleasant." This constant preoccupation with human sin and failure is of course shared by Mr Stumfold.

During another conversation, Mr Maguire regales Miss Mackenzie with the importance of singing in worship, something which plays a large part in these informal gatherings. He says: "But we may be cheerful— we may go about our work singing psalms of praise instead of songs of sorrow. Don't you agree with me, Miss Mackenzie, that psalms of praise are better than songs of sorrow?" To which she replies: "I don't sing at all myself." At Mr Stumfold's parties, singing plays a major part in spreading the gospel.

The tea party set is not drawn from the lower echelons of society. Money and the good things of life are never far below the surface. Mr Stumfold and his wife live comfortably with her father, a rich man, and both want for nothing. Miss Mackenzie is to find that as a rich single lady she will not lack for suitors, the first of whom is Mr Maguire, himself, anxious to follow in his vicar's prosperous footsteps. When she is reluctant to accept his overtures, he follows her to London and renews his suit. Mrs Todd is judgemental in her observations: "I always see that when a lady goes in to be an evangelical, she soon finds a husband to take care of her; that is, if she has got any money."

This attraction to material things accompanies a concern with status and class which always simmers below the Bible and the teacups. Mrs Stumfold usually makes her visits to her husband's flock using her carriage and horses to impress, and there is a suspicion that attending the vicarage tea party confers a social bonus.

A member of the group includes the wife of a retired coachbuilder who "was painfully anxious to make her way into the good evangelical society of Littlebath".

Trollope's snapshot of evangelical life in Littlebath would not be complete without stress on the isolation of Mr Stumfold's church from other churches, all of which in his eyes fall short of pure evangelical truth. On one occasion, his wife exchanges angry words with the Reverend Mr Paul, priest of the High Church up the road, and much given to ritual and candles, a man she describes as a "ribald ruffian". See how these Christians love one another!

For the record, Miss Mackenzie finally breaks away from the tea party scene, as personal matters necessitate her return to London. There she becomes engaged to marry the heir to a baronetcy, a distant member of her own family. She will never regret her escape from Mr Stumfold and his Littlebath evangelical gatherings.

### The Reverend Ben Read

It's Saturday morning. The house is quiet as Gillian and his two daughters have gone to the swimming pool, and Ben Read is having an extra hour in bed, half snoozing, half awake. He is Vicar of St Michael's Church in Brinton, a busy evangelical parish near the university. Tomorrow locals who come to his church will be joined by students from the University Evangelical Christian

Union who come for the Bible-centred preaching for which St Michael's is so well known. He must get up and work at that half-finished sermon on those words of Jesus "You must be born again" and what they mean for us today.

But the bed is warm and cosy, and Ben's mind wanders back to his time at university over 25 years ago. He reflects it was then that the foundation of his present life was laid. A vivid memory springs to mind of the day he had spotted Gillian in a lecture a few rows down from him. He couldn't take his eyes off her—it was her fault he had made so few notes of those lectures. For several weeks, he had carefully arranged to leave the lecture theatre close behind her; a coffee date had followed, and he had summoned up the courage to ask her out one Saturday evening. "No good," she had responded. "I go to the Christian Union Meeting that night. Why not come with me—this week it's in Alan and Mary's place in St James Street." In those days, his main interests were rugger and drinking. Religion was a vacant space. He recalled how he would have done anything to be with Gillian, even if it meant swallowing a spot of religion, but he had not reckoned that the evening would give him a changed life as well as Gillian.

His mind can still recall the scene: a packed room with students sitting on chairs, on the floor or leaning against the walls. He remembered young Tony—the science boffin—banging out rousing songs they called choruses on the old piano while everyone joined in with gusto—usually with the name of Christ repeated over and over again. He recalled a fellow priest saying to him years later: "I can't stand those chorus things where one word is sung over and over again—so boring." He had replied: "Very interesting. So you don't care for Handel's Messiah?" This floored the man, and he had been rather proud of his response. Then there had been "Testimony Time", when one or two students got up and said what Jesus Christ meant to them. It had all been very moving. The climax of the evening he recalled was always a Bible talk, often by the local curate. Everything was still vivid in his memory, especially the night when a law student had said to him afterwards: "What does Jesus mean to you, Ben?" It was the question that changed his life. After his days at university, his newfound Christian faith had led him to a church college to train as a priest and eventually to where he now was: vicar of a church packed with university students and where evangelical squashes like the one in which he had found his faith were a common event.

Now, his whole being is devoted to bringing other people to faith and to teaching them how to explore it further in their daily lives. Every Sunday evening he holds a Guest Service in his church, where other people—mainly students—are encouraged to bring friends who are not church people. He always preaches a challenging gospel message on these occasions and sometimes at the end of his talk invites anyone in the congregation who wishes to give their lives to faith to come forward and stand at the front, both as an act of witness to others and also for a dedication prayer. Some people call this an appeal. An incident related to him once by a famous preacher floats into his half-awake mind. This priest had explained how he had once ended a sermon at a smart church in Gerrards Cross by saying loudly to himself "Peter, you *can't* make an appeal in Gerrards Cross—it's just not the done thing." Then he had tried the same trick again and once more turned back, but finally had said "Blow it! I don't care if this is smart Gerrards Cross. I'm going to ask you to come forward if you want to make a decision for faith tonight." Ben reflects that he doesn't approve of this kind of pre-prepared play-acting in the pulpit.

Lying comfortably between the sheets, Ben realizes that he has now been Vicar of St Michael's for ten years. It had been rewarding in many ways, but a difficult ten years in others. He is lucky to have many faithful local residents in his congregation alongside his student supporters, and it is these locals who become churchwardens, who serve on the Church Council and who keep the fabric and finances of the church firmly in place. But there have still been many difficult church meetings along the way. He reflects that nearly all his problems stem from the many things in modern life which militate against St Michael's tradition of putting the Bible at the centre of parish life and worship.

For example, there is the question of women priests. Many of his people say that the Bible is against this development, now an accepted part of church life. St Michael's has never gone along with this change, holding that the Bible teaches that women should not hold positions of headship in the church. A female priest has never served in his church. Then there is the even more troubling matter of same-sex relationships. St Michael's has always taken the view that such things are wrong, but there are people on the Church Council who disagree, and there have been furious differences on the issue which have made Ben unhappy. Alongside this issue, there have been the recent child sexual abuse scandals in the Church, many in places like St Michael's which are in the evangelical tradition. This has made for great hurt among some of his people who are ashamed that such things could happen in a church. Ben has done his best to comfort and help them, but he has felt inadequate to the task. Then there are arguments in progress at the moment on the Church Council about cutting the amount of money St Michael's gives to the diocese each year. Some feel that the diocese wastes money on too much bureaucracy and on priests who do not pull their weight, while others disagree. The end of this particular argument is not yet in sight.

In his dreaming, Ben glances at the clock on the bedside table. Nine thirty! He leaps out of bed smartly. Sermons don't write themselves and Sunday will soon be here—and he has promised to peel the potatoes for lunch before Gillian and the girls arrive back. No time to waste.

# The Man of the People

## The Reverend Frank Fenwick, Vicar of Bullhampton

It would be hard to imagine a more attractive parish than the small town of Bullhampton in Dorset, surrounded by unspoilt countryside, with its ancient parish church nestling at the centre of a bustling life. Its vicar, Frank Fenwick, is equally attractive. Tall, fair-haired, well-bred, with bright eyes and a look about him that shows he might be severe if he were not so thoroughly good humoured; the perfect picture-book vicar. With his loving young wife Janet and their four young children, Fenwick lives in the kind of house a country vicarage ought to be, complete with orchard, kitchen garden and resident groom and a gardener. A country parson to his fingertips, he is fond of hunting, shooting and fishing while being at the heart of Bullhampton and on good terms with the squire, the village policeman, the doctor, the magistrates and all the leading citizens. Not lacking in vigour, he might be found one day berating the post office for its late postal deliveries in the town, or on another day giving a good hiding with a blunt instrument to some ruffians up to no good late at night in the vicarage garden. Another part of him belongs to a London Club, and he has a publisher in town for his occasional papers on social issues.

Yet life for Fenwick is far from idyllic. From time to time, every parish is rocked by unexpected major events disturbing the tenor of daily routine, and Bullhampton is no different. Two matters raise their ugly heads, and both prove extremely testing for the vicar. First, a ghastly murder is committed on his own doorstep, as next door to the vicarage Farmer Trumbull's guard dog is put down with a bit of poisoned meat, allowing thieves to get into the farmhouse. They set about the farmer with an axe, leaving him dead in a pool of blood before taking his life savings. Another shock comes when the Pastor of Bullhampton's Free Church Chapel and his congregation give the vicar and his folk notice that their brand-new chapel is to be built directly opposite the entrance to the vicarage. Some church people think it should be removed as "a nuisance", and the matter deeply divides the town. Trollope cannot resist setting out his personal view on the church v. chapel debate he creates here. He writes that when Fenwick and a friend visit the completed chapel building, both of them "acknowledged that it was ugly, misplaced, uncomfortable, detestable to the eye and ear, and general feeling,—except as so far as it might suit the wants of people who were not sufficiently educated to enjoy the higher tone of Church of England services". Happily, it is later found the chapel has been erected on ground belonging to the vicar and it has to be demolished and rebuilt elsewhere.

Much of a priest's life centres on people and their problems, and there are always a few folk who take more time than all the others put together. Fenwick frequently finds himself beating a path to a disorientated family who lived at the mill just outside the town, where Miller Brattle's two young children give him particular concern. The son Sam, one of the vicar's favourites, has turned out to be an undisciplined teenager, one of the group found in the vicarage garden on that memorable night, who was also mistakenly suspected of being involved with the murder. Carry Brattle, the miller's youngest daughter, has also become involved with a "disreputable" and has committed the then unforgiveable sin of sleeping with him before a marriage that never took place after running away from home. Then there is Harry Gilmour, Fenwick's close personal friend, whose love life gives the vicar perpetual worry.

In the wings another figure causes our vicar further headaches. The local magnate, Lord Trowbridge of Turnover Park, has never liked the priest and regards him as "objectionable", chiefly on the unproven ground that he belongs to the "High Church" party and leans towards what the noble lord sees as inappropriate ceremonies in services. Trowbridge is a pompous, arrogant, status-conscious aristocrat who owns most of the town, and is probably jealous of the vicar's popularity and place in the community. The dominant figure in the parish, it is Trowbridge who has given the land for the new chapel and paid for the building—largely to annoy the vicar.

What sort of a priest is Fenwick? We learn little about his pulpit skills, but an informed guess would indicate that he is not a great preacher. It is perhaps significant that on the Sunday following the murder the morning sermon took the form of an account of the crime, while there was no evening sermon at all. But of his pastoral skills and dealings with individuals there can be no doubt; they give an object lesson to his colleagues of the cloth, as he spends his time giving "comfortable words to old women and gently rebuking young maidens".

When he talks to Carry's mother, he does not condemn her daughter's fall from grace but instead speaks of God's love and forgiveness rather than the moral requirements of religion. He speaks tenderly of the "erring, fallen child", and when he finally manages to meet with a tearful, repentant Carry he gives the same message: "If we were to love only the good we should love very few." Fenwick also realizes that a person in distress needs assurance of human love and care, something of more immediate avail than "the love of the Lord God". He knows that holy, pious talk rarely helps.

In his concern for people, Fenwick always displays basic common sense. When his close friend Harry, the local squire, is deeply disappointed in love and turns in on himself, the vicar realizes that he needs a wise and sensible friend to stay with him. Harry is incapable of arranging such a visit for himself, so Fenwick takes the initiative. He writes to a Salisbury cathedral canon, one of Harry's relations, who duly arrives for a stay at the squire's house and gives him company. Later, suffering from a broken heart, Harry leaves home in despair, but Frank follows him up to London to give sensible down-to-earth advice and counsel, telling him that only cowards run away from their problems. Similarly, when Mary Lowther, a friend staying at the vicarage, has difficulty in writing a delicate letter to an ex-fiancé who wants to renew their relationship, Frank steps in and writes it for her. When she finds it impossible to visit Harry and tell him she cannot return his love either, Fenwick goes to see him and "does the deed". This same practical instinct leads him take Mrs Brattle on a long journey to visit Carry, her erring daughter. He knows that a mother separated from a daughter in trouble must be miserable and desperate with anxiety.

This practical common sense is accompanied by deep kindness and generosity. When Fenwick catches Sam up to no good in his garden in doubtful company, he doesn't hand him over to the police but lets him go with a warning. When Sam is suspected by the police of being involved with the murder, Fenwick stands bail to ensure that he doesn't have to remain in prison until the trial takes place. He spends much time and money trying to find Carry after her disappearance from home, and when he finally locates her, pays for her board and lodging and plans to find a permanent place for her, because she is too afraid of her father's wrath to return home.

Fenwick's overarching common sense is combined with a deep empathy for people, for what they think and feel, a quality at the heart of every good priest's pastoral work. When the vicarage is threatened with danger because it is rumoured there are house breakers about, Fenwick does not disclose his concern to Janet for fear of making her anxious. When he goes to the mill seeking Sam after the vicarage garden incident, he merely tells Mrs Brattle he "would like to have a talk with Sam", giving no details for fear of worrying her. Humour always sits alongside his empathy, as when he is told that people who have been in the army are usually "no better than they should be", Fenwick replies that this is true, "unless it be the army of martyrs, and there may be doubt on the subject even as to them".

It takes a big man to forgive when the wrongs committed are grievous and painful. Fenwick is such a man. He has always gone out of his way to be kind and helpful to Mr Puddleham, the chapel pastor, frequently sending him peaches and cabbages from the vicarage garden. His reward? To discover that Puddleham was in league with Lord Trowbridge in the building of the new chapel which caused him so much heartache. When Puddleham preaches a vicious sermon attacking the Church of England, he goes on being kind and generous, and it is the same story with Lord Trowbridge.

Later, when the chapel he caused to be built is removed the peer sues for peace and invites the vicar and his wife to stay at his home, Turnover Park. Fenwick is happy to respond. However, his deep conviction, that it is never a good thing for a parish priest to fall out with the landlord who owns the town in which his church is set, plays a major part in his decision to accept the olive branch.

## The Reverend Robert Bolter

Robert Bolter is the eldest son of James Bolter, Vicar of Hastings. A day boy at a local fee-paying school, he was captain of the Rugby First XV and Head Boy. The expected Oxford place never materialized, and he graduated from Exeter University with a degree in theology; theology because Robert was one of the few sons of the vicarage who do not grow away from the faith. As a boy, he always had intense admiration for his father and decided at an early age to follow in his footsteps as a priest.

Robert has a vivid memory of the time he trained for the priesthood at a church college in Cambridge. Every lunchtime the staff and students of the college gathered for short midday prayers in the college chapel. He recalls sniggering in the ranks as prayers were offered for 25 former students of the college serving in the Diocese of Winchester, 19 in the Diocese of Canterbury, 3 in the

Diocese of Liverpool and 5 in the Diocese of Newcastle. From that time forward, he had resolved to work as a priest in the north of England.

After serving as a curate first in an inner-city Leeds parish and then in suburbia, Robert is now Vicar of Houghton, a small rural market town in Yorkshire. A proud and closely knit community with the ancient parish church at its heart, the fast modern life of the south seems a world away from Houghton—although commercial pressures mean the nearest bank is 15 miles away in the next city. Robert has been there for ten years, living happily in the old vicarage next to the church with his wife Jill, a former teacher, and their three young girls.

He cuts a tall sturdy figure in the streets and lanes of Houghton, well liked by church and non-church people alike. His children go to local schools; he is chair of governors at the local church school and in the summer turns out for the Houghton team in the local cricket league. There are few aspects of town life with which he is not in some way involved and he is on good terms with all the leaders of the local community, from the magistrates to the members of the Borough Council, which has its offices in the town. The local cottage hospital still survives—largely as a convalescent centre for Houghton citizens discharged from the big City General Hospital—and Robert's visits there every Wednesday afternoon are greatly welcomed by staff and patients alike.

The daily round of the vicar's settled life has been rudely interrupted by a number of unwelcome happenings in past months. First, there was the difficult matter of a murder in the town, the first within living memory. The victim, Richard Freeman, was a prominent magistrate and town councillor and a popular local figure. He had been chair of the Bench which had committed Jim Spence, a local farm labourer, for trial at the City Crown Court on a charge of manslaughter. Spence, in furious anger, had driven a farm tractor at a trespasser on the farm and inflicted injuries from which the victim had died. After serving a long prison sentence, he had returned to Houghton and in cold blood had shot Freeman dead as he was walking down the drive of his own house. The affair was the talk of the town for many months, and as a close friend of Freeman the vicar had found the matter deeply painful.

The funeral had been a major occasion. So many people had come that loudspeakers were installed outside so that those in the churchyard could follow the service. The bishop had officiated at the occasion, and Robert had given the funeral address, a painful and difficult task. He recalled that Richard, as a magistrate, had often said how pleased he was that capital punishment for murder had been abolished years ago—he thought it was inhumane and not worthy of a civilized society. Robert often wondered if Richard would have still endorsed that view.

Then there was the nasty, embarrassing business with Andrew, the son of Henry and Hilary Winners. Henry was a solicitor and partner in a firm in the city, to which he commuted every day, and was also a churchwarden and prominent member of Robert's congregation. He and Hilary were close friends of Robert and Jill, and the two couples often visited each other's houses socially. Both families had young children with Andrew at 15 being the eldest of the Winners' children. As all Robert's children were girls, he had struck up a friendship with Andrew, accompanying him to football matches in the city in the winter and coaching him at cricket in the summer so that the two were frequently seen together.

A busybody in the congregation wrote to the bishop suggesting this friendship was "unhealthy and unwise", a cowardly and unpleasant action instead of mentioning the matter directly to Robert. The bishop, knowing Robert well, gave little credence to the letter, but took the opportunity of inviting him over to talk. Over a pre-lunch sherry, he counselled Robert to be careful in this area, and to avoid "all appearance of evil". This totally unexpected conversation shook Robert "to his roots". The bishop had gone on to say that he had no option but to ask the Diocesan Safeguarding Officer to talk both to the writer of the letter to establish his grounds for complaint as well as to Andrew himself. Happily, these conversations indicated no ground for concern at any point; even better no whisper of the matter reached anyone else in the parish or the media.

The incident has caused Robert immense pain and weeks of anxiety. Happily, the friendship with Henry and Hilary is unaffected, and they, with Jill, supported Robert during this difficult time. Both share Robert's horror at what had happened. It is a salutary thought that this unhappy saga took place before the more recent concerns about safeguarding in the Church of England and the many ongoing discussions about the matter. As a result, Robert would hopefully have been more cautious in his dealings with Andrew.

# The Wise Old Bird

## The Reverend Dr Mortimer Tempest

In every village and town there is often a wise, unruffled and utterly reliable figure at the heart of the community. In Silverbridge, it is the local priest. Despite his name, Mortimer Tempest, he is a man calm and stable in all situations. Trollope does not draw any physical picture of him, but it is easy to imagine a dark, stocky man of middle height with a large, impressive and determined face, a priest with whom you would not wish to tangle if it could be avoided. He has been in Silverbridge for many years and a certain weariness has crept in—some say he would now welcome a less taxing role in a Cathedral Close.

It is through Josiah Crawley, the downtrodden sad priest of a poor parish near Silverbridge, that we come to know Dr Tempest. As both rector and rural dean of Silverbridge, Tempest has oversight of Crawley's Hogglestock parish, and this priest is not one of his favourites. Many folk in Hogglestock are poor needy brickmakers with a vicar almost as poor as themselves, unable to give them alms. Instead, Crawley often gives support in menial tasks. He has been seen turning a washing mangle for a poor sick woman or carrying a heavy load along a country lane for another of his flock. Dr Tempest has fixed ideas about the dignity and bearing of a priest; actions of this kind are for him inappropriate and demeaning. More seriously, Crawley in his poverty has been accused of stealing a cheque and has to appear before the Silverbridge magistrates charged with theft.

As might be expected, Dr Tempest's character marked him out as a magistrate, and he has served on the Silverbridge Bench for many years. It has been suggested that it could be appropriate for him to stand down when the case against his clerical colleague was heard. He disagrees in a typically robust and determined manner, commenting that he has a particular interest in the case; no doubt feeling it incumbent on him to ensure that his fellow priest has a fair hearing. For the record, Crawley was committed for trial at the next Assizes, but the case never reached this stage because evidence came to light revealing his innocence.

Dr Proudie, Bishop of Barchester, is concerned about Crawley's standing in the Church following his committal for trial. Controlled by his wife in so many matters, he follows her suggestion of appointing a Clerical Commission of Enquiry to report to him on Crawley's status in the Church following the legal proceedings. Dr Tempest is the obvious person to be chairman of it. However, the bishop is not a popular man, and Tempest is advised by many friends not to accept the appointment. In contrast, Dr Tempest's view is simply that the Commission was the best way of proceeding, and his private thoughts about Dr Proudie are irrelevant, as he was bound to have respect for the office the bishop held. When a fellow guest at a dinner party says she is sorry he has "joined the bishop", he responds: "It is generally thought well a parish clergyman should agree with his bishop." These upright and principled words afford a revealing window into the nature of a discreet and sagacious man. It is rumoured that Dr Tempest never even tells his wife about any delicate church issues with which he had to deal.

When he visits the palace to discuss the Commission, he is assured by the bishop: "There is no clergyman in the Diocese in whose prudence and wisdom I have more confidence than yours." These qualities are much in view during this visit. Dr Tempest has stayed overnight at the palace and in the morning, before his meeting with the bishop, he is quietly reading his newspaper when Mrs Proudie without warning attempts to engage him in conversation on the Crawley case. With much courtesy and aplomb, he evades her approach, saying it would not be right to make the matter a topic of "common conversation". The lady then tries another approach, only to be told that if he discusses the issue, he will be guilty of "great impropriety". He then quickly escapes into the garden.

Dr Tempest is surprised to find Mrs Proudie in the room when he arrives in the bishop's study, where his cool, level-headed response to problems is to be tested still further. He refuses to respond to the bishop's attempts to discuss the Commission with Mrs Proudie present and when the good lady intervenes and calls him "stubborn" and "unreasonable", he merely tells her he is sorry she has not learnt the lessons of their earlier conversation that day, and that it would not be proper to hold the meeting in her presence. When the bishop utterly fails to persuade his wife to leave the room, Dr Tempest does so himself, saying as he goes that matters concerning the Commission should now be dealt with by letter. Game, set and match to the Rector of Silverbridge!

A little later, the Clerical Commission meets at Dr Tempest's rectory. It consists of four other priests, with the rector as chairman. His way of proceeding is typical of the man. The five priests first meet in the rector's dining room; he knows that any meeting is easier to chair after its members are mellow following a good lunch. They then adjourn to his study, where he listens courteously as each member of the group gives his opinion on the Crawley affair. The rector then adds his own thoughts in a manner which quickly become the thoughts of the Commission. It is a masterful lesson in concealed autocracy; we are told "Dr Tempest had carried his point exactly as he might have done had the four gentlemen been represented by the chairs on which they sat". It is then agreed that as chairman he should write to Mr Crawley and invite him to the next meeting of the Commission.

It might be thought that under the rector's calm and controlled exterior there lurks a hard and insensitive soul. The subsequent progress of the Commission shows that nothing could be further from the truth. With his formal letter inviting Crawley to the meeting, he includes a private handwritten note, hoping that the priest will join him at lunch before the Commission meets, a kind gesture intended to give a little warmth to what will be a difficult occasion for Crawley. However, the meeting and lunch never take place because quite unexpectedly the Hogglestock priest turns up one day at the rectory with the intention of short circuiting the whole work of the Commission.

Crawley is a man given to dramatic gestures of poverty and self-sacrifice and who makes sure he arrives at the rectory exhausted and spattered with mud after insisting on walking the many miles from his parish. Dr Tempest quietly ignores his state and offers wine and a biscuit to restore the traveller. With a display of pique, Crawley refuses the offer, at which the rector quietly insists there can be no conversation of any kind until he has taken the refreshment. A man more than in control of a difficult situation.

When the two men eventually talk, Dr Tempest is horrified when Crawley tells him he has come to say that as an accused man he intends to resign his parish and asks his host, as rural dean, to inform the bishop of this decision. The rector immediately refuses. In the plainest possible language, he tells the poor man that as a married priest responsible for a wife and family such a step would be "very wicked". He strongly advises Crawley to wait until after the trial before taking such a momentous decision. Next day a letter from Dr Tempest arrives at Hogglestock Vicarage imploring Crawley not to write his letter of resignation and offering to negate it on his behalf if it had already been sent. No wonder Crawley tells his wife he had found in Dr Tempest "a softness of heart for which I had not looked".

## The Reverend Canon James Fenner

Some priests are respected by their people, and others are loved by them, but it is rare to manage both at the same time. James Fenner had always been respected but was rarely loved. From his earliest days, he had cut an impressive figure, the proverbial tall, dark, handsome man with a direct and authoritative manner, a priest you would think twice before challenging. He is now Rector of Market Hinton in Somerset, and people there recall an incident at the Flower Festival in the church a few years ago. Stall holders and stewards were busy chatting to each other and welcoming visitors when a ripple went round the building: "The Rector has just come in." Immediately the chat ceased and everyone was on their best behaviour. A memory which sums up well how his people regard their rector.

From the start, Fenner had been expected to climb to the top of the clerical ladder fairly swiftly. It never happened. After a short curacy in a Somerset rural parish, he served as chaplain of his old Cambridge College for a number of years. Then, at the early age of 35, he joined the senior staff of a well-known English cathedral. Friends assumed this was a good launching pad for higher office, but the call never came. After some years, he gradually became disillusioned with life in the Cathedral Close. Sometimes he falsely imagined he was just there because his fine figure and commanding presence lent an extra dignity to cathedral services and processions; at other times he resented the dean's control of policy and direction and longed to command his own ship. When the Bishop of Bath and Wells offered him the parish of Market Hinton, a substantial Somerset market town, he took the most unusual step of leaving the cathedral with his wife and young family and returning to parish life.

Over the years, he has served the town well. An excellent preacher with a clear and striking delivery which commands attention, he can always be relied on to direct his hearers' minds to some new and practical spiritual truth. This pulpit reputation is such that he is often asked to preach in other Somerset churches on special occasions. Fenner also holds the old-fashioned belief that a visiting priest leads to a church-going people, and he is faithful in visiting the homes of his parish whenever occasion demands, as well as on many occasions when it doesn't. His conduct of all church services, along with baptisms, marriages and funerals, never fails to bring appropriate dignity to the proceedings. He is a familiar figure at the local hospital, and anyone from Market Hinton who has the misfortune to land up there will be likely to encounter him at the bedside. An excellent chair of the church council, he listens carefully to all views, keeping every discussion to the point, never allowing any meeting to drift on interminably. Above all, Fenner is known throughout the town as a person of wisdom and good judgement; his views are respected by local doctors, schoolteachers, town councillors and others who play a significant part in the town. He is frequently consulted for personal advice by individuals both from his parish and by folk with no church affiliation, in the firm knowledge that any confidences given will remain just that. In short, he is an excellent parish priest. Yet despite all these things he is respected rather than loved. If truth be told, there are even some persons who hold him in awe and who are even slightly afraid of him.

The question must be asked why such a capable man has not progressed further in the Church. With his undoubted ability, at the very least he could have become an archdeacon if not a bishop. Yet he is still in Market Hinton after 15 years and rapidly reaching an age when promotion to more senior office becomes increasingly unlikely. Church colleagues often discuss the question and come up with a number of different answers.

It is generally agreed his personality does not help. Yes, he is wise, clever and discerning but is generally thought to be a cold fish, lacking in warmth. He disciplines himself to help others and give them his time, but there is something lacking. People say: "You never feel you quite meet him. There's no rapport. You wonder what is behind the impressive exterior. What's going on inside?" It is not surprising that Fenner has few close friends even among fellow clergy. He has little small talk, rarely initiates conversations and shows little sense of humour. When someone cracks a joke or makes a light remark, he will usually smile, giving the impression he was just going through a routine reaction because it is expected. All these things have also earned the rector the reputation of being "as hard as a bar of iron", a false impression because underneath this stony exterior he is deeply sensitive. Yet only occasionally do flashes of it ever reach the light of day.

Neither could it ever be claimed that James Fenner is a person of great initiative and originality. A superb parish priest, he runs like a well-oiled engine along the traditional lines of parish ministry; there is no fresh vision or creative imagination, things which a parish priest needs in challenging times.

Probably much more significant is the fact that he has a serious difference of opinion with the bishop over the number of priests employed by the diocese who do not have parishes but who, in his view, hold rather nebulous appointments. He believes that such posts as a Diocesan Chaplain for Mission or a Diocesan Chaplain for Clergy Care consume precious financial resources for no good reason, and he expresses these ideas in meetings at which the bishop is present. Any priest is normally dependent on his bishop to put him forward for a higher appointment; Fenner does himself no favours here.

Equally significant is the fact the rector is an idealist who feels that if he is worthy of high office it would come to him naturally. He would despise himself if he pushed his own cause, engaged friends to speak for him or in any way promoted himself and his future. These things are against his principles. Perhaps now he is paying the price for this high view of life.

In the final analysis, the reason why James Fenner is destined to stay as a parish priest for the rest of his life may be much more prosaic. Bishops and archdeacons probably do not spend sufficient time in thinking about the future of the clergy they serve or engage in "talent spotting". Their lives are too full of so many other demands, committees and engagements. Those who wish to rise in the Church usually have to engage in some modest self-propulsion.

# Postscript

This volume was written during the Covid lockdown of 2020/21. Since then, it has been marinating in a drawer of my desk. Looking through it again in 2023, I am reminded of the old proverb "Time waits for no man". I like to think my fictitous sketches of contemporary clergy are true to life, but I retired from full-time ministry as a priest over 20 years ago. Even during this short time, the "clergy scene" has changed in significant ways.

For example, I make the unstated assumption all my "modern" clergy are university graduates who later trained for ordination at a residential theological college. A significant number of today's priests are not graduates and the majority will have been trained via one of the non-residential regional training courses set up in the dioceses. Only a few theological colleges remain. Since 1994 women priests and women bishops have made a massive contribution to the mission of the Church, while the ethnic mix of the clergy has broadened. It would be amusing to see the look on Archdeacon Grantley's face as he meets his new bishop and discovers she is "a person of colour" and a woman. Sadly, Trollope knew no women priests and so they are not included in these pages. A great loss.

I now note that some details in my contemporary sketches have changed. For example, greater care is taken these days over clergy appointments. Few priests now owe their place to discreet conversations over lunch at a London Club or to the "behind the scenes" kind offices of a bishop or a friend who has the ear of a bishop. While the old adage "It's not what you know but who you know" retains some truth, public advertisement followed by a rigorous selection procedure and demanding interviews is the norm. When I became a dean in 1991, there was no formal interview; today the "Selection Process for a Dean" covers nine sheets of close print with endless hurdles to jump. Even a trial sermon may be required.

Life in the diocese has also changed. Most bishops and senior clergy are pastorally concerned for the parish clergy who serve with them and in particular for their mental health. A priest's life can be stressful. David Lloyd would not now be left to suffer alone, and today counselling and professional help is usually available. Sadly, fewer colourful characters occupy senior posts; swashbuckling archdeacons like Frederick Roberts are a rarity in modern times. In the past, able priests like James Fenner, who might have been offered more senior posts, often did not realize their full potential; now the talents and gifts of the clergy are more likely to be used to the full as bishops and senior staff keep the future of their clergy under review. Safeguarding matters in all dioceses have become highly organized and professional; Robert Bolter and Archdeacon Roberts' parish priest might both have been treated differently in today's Church.

Re-reading my manuscript reminded me there are fewer clergy about like David Ward, 30 years Vicar of Walton. There is much to be said for clergy like him, fixtures in the parish as generations come and go where the vicar finds himself baptizing the children and grandchildren of couples he married in the distant past. Such priests are rare today. Again, it is a pity that the interchange between academic life and parish life has become increasingly unusual. The move of Matthew Gibbs from Oxford to the West Country would now be most unlikely as constant parish demands make it increasingly difficult for a scholar to find time to continue writing and research. The strong differences expressed within Ben Read's congregation over homosexuality issues is currently mirrored in deep public divisions in the modern Church on this matter.

Twenty years into the future the Church of England and its clergy will have changed yet again in ways we cannot now know. As in Trollope's day, there will always be saints and scholars, men of the world and men of power, time servers and snobs. Human nature never changes. Yet clergy of every age are united through the One they serve, after whom their faith is named: He who is the "same yesterday, today and for ever" and who came into the world to address the problems raised by this very same human nature.

Milton Keynes UK
Ingram Content Group UK Ltd.
UKHW022345030624
443662UK00012B/91